Sara Arey ♥ RefutureYourLife.com

The Universe F♥cking Loves Me

TRANSFORMATION JOURNAL

The Universe F♥cking Loves Me

TRANSFORMATION JOURNAL

The Step-by-Step Journal
for Getting Out of Your Way, Into Your Flow,
and Maintaining a High Vibration

BY SARA AREY

Cover Designer & Compositor: Sally Wright Day
Editor: Maggie McReynolds

Author's photos courtesy of
Rupa Kapoor, Woman Redefined

ISBN: 978-1-7329480-2-0

For you, the reader of this book.

May it guide you in experiencing
that you are loved and held
beyond your wildest dreams.

Welcome
to this Transformation Journal

This journal, and the book it accompanies, probably got your attention because of the name. People tell me that they have an immediate "yes!" to it because they believe that the Universe f♥cking loves them. And yet…

There are those times when it doesn't *feel* like it. Those times when you don't trust the Universe or yourself. When it doesn't feel like things are working out. Instead, it feels hard, scary, confusing, and overwhelming. In those moments, it's hard to know what to do to get out of your own way.

In the book, I talk about feeling your feelings and then doing what I call The Three Cs: getting curious, creative, and courageous. It's a powerful approach for turning blocks and breakdowns into breakthroughs. People often tell me about what a great practice it is and how it's helping them.

That's fabulous! But I want to do more than just talk about it. I want to actually guide you through doing it for yourself. I want you to have something in your hands that will lead you step-by-step through how to expand in situations that would ordinarily close you down; situations that come up in the normal, day-to-day ebb and flow of life.

And thus, this Transformation Journal was born.

This journal will expand you on many levels by helping you:

- **Become more fluent in and connected to your feelings.** More and more studies are showing the importance of emotional intelligence. Being able to identify and name your emotions (beyond happy, sad, and pissed) increases your level of communication and connection. As a culture, we've been taught very little about our feelings and how to identify them. It comes much more naturally to some people than to others, and everyone can learn to do it.

- **Accept and process your feelings, rather than staying stuck in them.**

- **Get more connected to your body, and the wisdom and guidance that it holds.**

- **Access your intuition and inner guidance.** You really do have all the answers you need. Feeling your feelings, being aware of your body, and deliberately opening to your inner wisdom creates a pathway to connect with them.

- **Sleep better, feel calmer and more connected with others.** When we're caught up in our emotions, we get reactive and feel stressed. Making a practice of the process in this journal will get you out of that. Not only will you enjoy your life more, others will enjoy being around you more.

- **Connect you with your power** by identifying your next step. Feeling like you don't have options and can't do anything to change a situation is the definition of powerlessness. Once you see a move you can make, as you will through this process, you're back in action and in your power.

- **Learn some easy poses you can do anytime and anywhere to re-center yourself and support the flow of your energy.** When your energy is high, you feel better, you attract more people to you, and life unfolds at a higher level. The poses I'll teach you, along with the process I guide you through, will work together to raise your vibration.

- **Create and hold space.** Doing this process over and over will create space between the moment you feel something and the moment you react. In that space is your power: your ability to choose your response and your ability to create what you want rather than simply re-creating what you're used to.

This journal isn't just for times when things feel hard. You'll see that there are pages for positive emotions too. Going through the process when you're feeling good will help you integrate the high-vibration energy more deeply. Connecting to your inner wisdom from this place will help you take powerful next steps and make the most of this energetic peak.

This journal is designed to be truly transformational for you. I've given you lots of great information and tools. While it's based on my extensive work with energy and clients, **no book can take the place of human connection and individual guidance**. You may still get stuck in your emotions or come up against something that feels so big and old that you'll need personalized support. Our blind spots genuinely are our blind spots. We can be greatly served by outside guidance to help us see what we're not seeing and to support us in working through it.

You don't have to stay stuck. A coach trained in the Refuturing Process can give you the intuitive insights, guidance, and support you need to convert old stories and patterns into more love and joy. What once held you back can be a catalyst for you to shine brighter. Visit my website, refutureyourlife.com, for my current offerings and to find out more. You don't have to struggle on your own. Your expansion process can be much faster and smoother with help.

You're everything you need to be. You are lovable no matter what. My hope and intention is that this journal guides you to experience this for yourself in increasingly deeper ways

Love,

Sara

Table of Contents

How to Use This Transformation Journal

Introduction

Did you know that you have a personal vibration level? It's the frequency of your energy.

Scientists have discovered that *everything* is energy, including things that feel solid to us. Even our physical body. You are literally made of energy.

All types of energy have a frequency. This is the rate at which the energy is moving. The different frequencies of light are what give us different colors in a rainbow, with red vibrating more at the low end of the spectrum and purple vibrating much more quickly. Studies have even found that healthy cells vibrate at a faster rate than malignant cells.

At some level, we know that people's energy varies. When we talk about someone having high or positive energy, what we're really describing is their personal energetic frequency, their rate of vibration.

Think of someone you know who you like being around. Someone who makes everyone feel better just by being in the group. When you're with this person, you feel lighter, happier, and more at ease. That person vibrates at a high frequency. This has nothing to do with how quickly they move or how fast they talk. This is about their energy.

Now think of someone you'd describe as a downer, someone who seems to pull you down before they even say a word. You can feel it when this person walks into a room. That person has a low energetic frequency.

While they're not exactly the same thing, power and energy are very closely related. When you feel confident and powerful, your energy has a higher vibration than when you feel powerless in a situation. The more you own your power, the more you raise your vibration.

It's important to know that when I talk about your power, I'm talking about the power that comes from being your authentic self. This is power from within. This is *not* the same thing as you having power *over* someone or over a situation. For more information on the difference between "power from within" and "power over," check out the book chapter called "Power."

The big question is, how do you own your power and increase your vibration? First of all, your power is already there. You can't *not* have your power. The key is to connect with it and to stop denying or limiting it.

In order to connect with your power, you first have to connect with yourself. **A major**

way you disconnect from your power is by focusing on what's outside of you rather than on what's inside of you.

When you perceive a lack in your life, you set about trying to fix it. You need more money, more safety, more love, or more power, so you try to get more. You feel inadequate, not good enough, or "less than," so you try to prove your worthiness and feel better by getting more acknowledgements and accomplishments.

When you feel unworthy, you look for rescuers and experts who can solve this problem for you and tell you how to get what you want, how to fix yourself and your life. It seems smart to put your trust and confidence in other people because they seem to have it together. You hope they'll share their secrets with you so you can have it together too. Once you're in a happy relationship, have financial and business success, and have a beautiful, healthy body, you'll be set, right?

There's nothing wrong with any of this. There's nothing wrong with pursuing material success, happiness, and beauty. It's just not fulfilling as long as you have an underlying sense of unworthiness. **You can never fill an inner need with outer *stuff*.** It's like eating sugary treats. They don't have the nutrition your body is truly craving, so you'll never be satisfied by them. Filled, yes. Satisfied, no. Not matter how much you consume, you'll never have enough, so you keep reaching for more and more.

Deep satisfaction at all levels—body, mind and spirit—comes from filling yourself from the inside rather than from the outside. It comes from connecting with your inner source of love, safety, abundance, and power. It comes from accessing your own answers and power. When you do this, you approach the world, your relationships, and your work from a place of wholeness and completion. **You showing up in the world becomes a way to share your fullness rather than to fill your emptiness.**

So how do you connect with yourself and access your own answers and power?

Being still and noticing what's going on inside of you is key. You can't connect to your inner wisdom through your mind. Your mind is a wonderful, amazing instrument—and it has its limits. Your answers come from a much deeper part of you.

The really hard part is that what comes up first when you sit in silence and stillness is all the S.T.U.F.F. (Stuck Thoughts, Unresolved Feelings, and Fears) you've been avoiding. [There's a lot more about this in my book.] The S.T.U.F.F. makes you feel uneasy and uncomfortable. Sometimes it's even painful, and like everyone else you avoid *those* feelings like the plague.

As a society, we've trained ourselves from the moment we first start to feel uncomfortable to reach for our phones, turn on the TV, read the news and plug into political drama, create our own drama, exercise, have sex, eat, drink, or any number of other things to distract us from discomfort. We fear we aren't enough, so we fill ourselves, our lives, and our homes with lots of *stuff*. We act like we can insulate ourselves from uncomfortable, even painful feelings, and that that's a good thing.

What we don't realize is that our power lies on the other side of our discomfort. Being able to stay with our feelings of inadequacy, uncertainty, and "not enough-ness" are what allow them to pass so that we can get to the truth beneath them.

Your Freedom Lies on the Other Side of Your Discomfort

No amount of money, outer power, or autonomy can impart the same type of freedom that simply being able to be with your thoughts, your emotions, and yourself does. Nothing you can create with your mind will be as creative, ingenious, and inspired as what you'll create when you tap into your higher self and higher purpose.

Working with myself and so many clients on this, what I've found is that three things make a big difference in being able to access inner peace and greater wisdom:

1. **Being able to be with your feelings**. Feelings are powerful. They are, after all, a form of energy, just as thoughts are. You can think of "emotions" as "e-motions"—energy in motion. They aren't meant to be stagnant. You're not meant to either wallow in them or hold onto them, not even the ones you think of as positive. What keeps you stuck is not allowing yourself to truly *feel* your emotions and move on. **This journal will guide you in connecting with your feelings, seeing them for what they are, and allowing them to flow.**

2. **Being present in your body.** In our society, so much attention and value has been placed on the mind that we've lost a lot of our connection with our bodies. We tend to see our body as transportation for our mind. This was definitely true for me for a long time. I didn't realize that my body is a huge source of intuition. I didn't know that being present in my body allows me to be present in the moment, to *feel* when something's off in a situation, in myself, or with another person. I didn't know that I was cutting off a huge source of my power. **This journal will guide you in becoming more present in and connected to your body. I'll teach you some energy poses that will make this process even easier and more effective.**

3. **Being witnessed.** When we feel seen and heard, we feel at our most powerful. When we don't, we feel like a voice crying into the wilderness. What I give my clients is the experience of being deeply seen and heard, in part because I hear what they're *not* saying and see them in bigger ways than they can see themselves. While no book can give you that directly, this one will guide you to **see** *yourself* **more clearly and lovingly than ever before.** This is a huge step in connecting with your power and your purpose. This clarity then enables you to **share yourself more authentically with others so that they have the possibility of seeing and hearing you more deeply. The more you show up, the more you're seen and heard. This book will help you show up more.**

All of this will facilitate you moving toward a more meditative state. Study after study is showing the benefits of meditation for business owners, athletes, children—everyone! By following the process in this journal, you'll create more inner space, which will make meditation and being in silence more palatable and more welcome. It'll also increase the amount of flow and ease you experience in your life in general. People and situations will bother you less. You'll take action more quickly, and the actions themselves will be more effective and have better outcomes. You'll start feeling stronger and more effective overall, and more relaxed and satisfied.

Those are powerful claims. That's because this journal will create and deepen your pathways of connection with yourself, and YOU are powerful.

The Three Cs

In the chapter of *The Universe F♥cking Loves Me* called "When the Shit Hits the Fan", I outline a process for turning breakdowns into breakthroughs. It's called "The Three Cs."

The steps of The Three Cs process are:

1. Get Curious
2. Get Creative
3. Get Courageous

The basic information from the book about each step is included here. It'll give you context for the sections of the Processing Pages. At the same time, it's not necessary for you to keep it in mind as your journal. You'll be guided through, step by step.

Before you start Step 1, you have to acknowledge and feel your feelings. Doing so frees up your energy (that inner struggle is a big energy suck!), creates some inner space, and relaxes your mind. It's also a step that's really hard for a lot of people. That's why this journal is laid out like it is.

If you need to express more than you have room for on the Processing Page, use the blank pages in the back or somewhere else. The important thing is for you to fully express yourself. If that takes 30 pages, then write 30 pages.

Step 1—Get Curious

Explore your situation. Look at it like an outsider might see it. As much as you can, let go of what you know (or think you know) about the situation and people involved. Remember that you might have been coming to this based on old patterns and assumptions. Try to let go of all that and start fresh.

Step 2—Get Creative

What creative possibilities can you come up with for this situation? Get ideas from your head, and also check in with your intuition and your heart. Crazy ideas are welcome! Impulses are too. Let yourself dream.

Step 3—Get Courageous

Now it's time to move into action, and that takes courage. You're doing something new, so you'll naturally have some nervousness. You might even feel a little anxious or scared. You might dread taking the next step. That's OK. It's normal. What *else* do you feel?

Over and over I've heard clients say things like, "I'm excited about this opportunity, but I'm also really nervous. I don't know if I can do it." Your excitement has your foot on the gas. Your "but" has you hitting the brake. It's really hard to make progress that way.

Try this instead: "I'm nervous and have doubts, and I'm really excited about this opportunity." By acknowledging *all* of your feelings and using the word "and," you keep the momentum going forward.

It makes a difference to say it in that order, too. We have a part of us that I call the Safety Self whose job is to protect us. It's the part many people refer to as a saboteur because it uses fear to keep us playing small. It's the really negative-sounding voice in our heads warning us about trying new things or becoming more visible. That's because to this part, shining your light makes you a target, and its mission is to keep you out of harm's way. It thinks it's helping you. By addressing the fears and nervousness first in the "and" statement, your Safety Self feels heard and relaxes. Some of your inner struggle melts, making it much easier to move forward.

When you practice getting curious, creative, and courageous, you address the muck that has you stuck, which frees you to move forward. Situations where you used to feel powerless can now be the stimulus that gets you into action and into more alignment with your essence and your joy.

Take a deep breath. I mean a really deep breath. Count to four as you inhale, letting your lungs fill and your belly expand. Count to four as you exhale, completely emptying your lungs as you draw your pelvic muscles up and in. Do it again and again as you go through this process. You've got this.

Feelings

It's so easy to get caught up in our feelings, to believe that they are the truth of who we are in the moment.

Feelings are important. Acknowledging and actually *feeling* our feelings is vital. Avoiding them or pushing them away in order to feel "better" or staying in our heads about them actually just keeps them in place. It's like having a closet where you put all the stuff you don't want or don't know what to do with. Keeping the door closed doesn't make that junk go away. It's still there. And as you keep putting more stuff in, you increase the likelihood that the door will burst open and everything will come pouring out.

One sign that you've got a closet stuffed full of thoughts and feelings is that you consistently feel the same way day after day. Are you regularly or often frustrated, angry, down, or overwhelmed? Even being constantly optimistic, cheerful, or happy can be a sign you're stuck and not allowing yourself to feel your full range of emotions.

It's easy to think that if our situation changed, we'd feel different. If only our partner was more understanding. If only we had more money. If only our lives were different. That seems logical because we believe our feelings are a *result* of what's going on around us.

Definitely when something happens in our lives we can have an emotional response to it. Our dog had a serious health issue the other day, and I definitely felt sad and worried. Now that she's much better, I feel relieved and grateful.

However, if I stay stuck in those feelings—worrying so much that I can't function, for instance—it's because something in *me* is being triggered. Maybe I'm connecting this situation with other deaths and losses in my life that still feel very painful. Maybe I'm feeling guilty for not walking her more, or I'm worrying about what life without her constant affection will be like. None of those is about what's happening *now*. They're all based in the past or the future. They aren't helping her or the situation. In fact, they're keeping me from being present with her here and now.

While current events can definitely have an emotional impact, we have an underlying state of being that has an even greater influence on us. Imagine being in the ocean just below surface of the water. You'd feel every wave and every storm. The deeper you go, the less you're knocked around by the surface turbulence. That's what happens when you clear out the old S.T.U.F.F. and create more inner space for yourself. You connect with the deeper parts of yourself, and become less tossed about by daily life.

Being fully responsible for our feelings, thoughts and reactions can be challenging. Sometimes it would feel so freaking good to be able to blame someone else for them! Sometimes we want to rage against the storms. Drama can be tempting, even when we complain about it, because it distracts us. When how you feel is all the fault of someone else—this jerk or that event—then you don't have to change. You don't have to do anything. You don't have to look at yourself and where you're holding onto old stuff. You get to be right!

The big problem is that there's no freedom in that. You have no options. You also have no power. You're at everyone else's mercy. Everything depends on them changing, and you have *zero* control over that.

Another problem with that scenario is that there isn't genuine connection or authenticity in those relationships. You don't even have a real connection with yourself. You're not accessing your inner wisdom, strength, or power. You're not making the difference in the world—in *your* world—that you could be.

The choice comes down to (1) looking inside and being willing to change, or (2) staying like you are and being comfortably miserable.

Don't worry. Change doesn't have to be as hard as it might seem. Start by using this journal. Let your emotions begin to flow and your wisdom begin to surface. Start taking the actions that occur to you and see what happens. Making even small changes now will create a big shift in the trajectory of where your life is headed.

Start by being willing to look inside and by being willing to acknowledge and feel your feelings. You can do this a step at a time, and this journal will show you how. You've got this.

The Heart Center Pose

I teach everyone I work with some movements and poses to help facilitate the flow of energy (which includes emotions and thoughts). The Heart Center Pose is one we use a lot. It'll look familiar to you because it's one people tend to use instinctively.

To do the Heart Center Pose, place one hand on the center of your chest over your sternum (breastbone). Place the other hand on top of it. It doesn't matter which hand is on top. You can have your eyes open or closed.

While this pose may look too easy to "do anything," it's actually very effective. It helps you move your energy and awareness from your head down into your body. This means that you have more access to your intuition and are more present in the moment. It also helps you connect with your heart and its wisdom. Most people find this pose to be very calming and grounding.

When you do this pose and say a statement like, "I accept these feelings," don't try to make yourself believe the statement. If a statement seems too big or too far from where you are right now, just add, "What if it's possible" to the beginning of it. "What if it's possible for me to accept these feelings."

Hold the statement lightly in your mind, or think it once and let it go, and then simply see what you notice. You might notice tension or a release of tension. You might notice a sense of movement or vibration. You might not notice anything at all. Whatever you notice is fine.

The key is to be a witness to whatever you're experiencing. You're not trying to *make* yourself accept your feelings or have different thoughts. You're not even trying to make yourself change. You're simply noticing and accepting what is with an openness to new possibilities, and accessing your own inner wisdom.

Noticing What You Feel in Your Body

For this section, simply write down what you sense in your body. It could be something like:

- Tension in my shoulders
- Hollowness in my stomach
- Heaviness in my heart
- Tingling in my back
- Excitement in my chest
- My legs want to run
- Energy feels stuck in my abdomen
- Lightness
- Tightness in my jaw
- I want to run away

There's nothing you're "supposed" to feel or notice. Try letting your attention wander over your body as if you're doing a scan. If this feels challenging to you, focus on your head, shoulders, chest, and abdomen. If you're not sure if you feel something, go ahead and write it down anyway. This isn't about getting it right. No one will be checking this. This is for you to help better connect you with yourself. Breathe, notice, and write.

Moving Your Body

Our bodies store our old emotions and memories. If you've ever felt a wave of emotion while getting a massage or holding a deep stretch, you know how the knots and tension in your body can be signaling that something's stuck.

You'll see on the Process Pages that I recommend moving your body several different times. This helps the stuck thoughts, feelings, and energy move more easily and freely. It also helps your intuition and insights surface more readily.

I highly suggest standing up and really letting your body move. See if you can move all the parts of your body—feet, legs, hips, middle, chest, arms, shoulders, neck, and head.

Gently move any part of your body that feels tense. If you only have time to do a little, then just do a little. Every bit helps. If you have time, put on your favorite song and dance.

Remember to breathe as you move.

If you need to stay seated, then stretch, move your legs and arms, gently turn your head from side to side—whatever you can do. If you're in close quarters, like on a plane, and unable to move at all, you can inhale, tense specific muscles, hold the tension and your breath, and then gently and fully release your breath as you completely relax your muscles.

This movement is for you. You're not trying to impress anyone. You don't need to look graceful or cool. Just move in ways that feel good to you, and smile.

The Energy Hookup

This is one of my favorite energy exercises because it does so much. I learned this from Donna Eden, a pioneer in the realm of energy medicine. In fact, she literally wrote the book on energy medicine. Check her out on YouTube or innersource.net if you want more information.

For this pose, you'll use the middle fingers of each hand. Place one middle finger (it doesn't matter which) between your eyebrows just above the bridge of your nose. Place the other one in your navel. With both fingers, push in and lift up.

Hold this position until you feel done. Sometimes that might be fairly quick. Other times, you might enjoy holding it for a minute or so. I like to wait until my body naturally takes a deep breath. Sometimes I even go longer than that and feel a second wave of even deeper relaxation.

Your body has multiple energy channels known as meridians. This pose hooks all your energy channels up and allows your energy to flow. It's great to use if you feel upset, scattered, or ungrounded—or any time you just want an energy boost. My meditation partner and I use it before we start meditating as a way to connect with ourselves and each other. Donna recommends doing it first thing every morning. You can do it standing, sitting, or lying down.

Feeling Curious

In this section, you get to explore this situation from a space of possibility rather than from your old patterns, stories, and assumptions. You might have old thoughts pop in, and you don't have to be stopped by them. Just notice them and then go on to the next one. You're looking for what makes you feel open, expansive, and lighter.

Nothing you come up with here will obligate you to anything, so don't worry about what you write down. Note any ideas, crazy thoughts or inspirations you have.

To help yourself see with fresh eyes, try asking yourself questions like:

- If this situation is an opportunity, what might it be an opportunity for?

- If someone I've never met were to walk up and look at what's going on, what woud they see?

- Where is my power in this?

- If there's a gift or opportunity for me hidden in this situation, just as it is, what might it be?

- How do I want to show up in this?

- What's important to me here?

- If nothing were too hard, too scary or too much trouble, what would I do?

- Am I brave enough to _____ ?

- If this situation completely resolved this second, what would I do? Can I do *that* now?

Refuturing Statements

Did you know that a clinical study has shown affirmation statements can cause more harm than good? I outline why in the chapter "Why Affirmations Backfire." Basically, if the statement is too far from our current experience, then our mind closes down and rejects the statement. It finds proof of why it isn't true, and we end up becoming *more* entrenched in what we *don't want*. Not the effect we were hoping for.

And because we're human, we then think something's wrong. We worry that we've done the affirmation wrong, or that there's something wrong with us. Ironically—and sadly—this sends us faster on the downward spiral that we were trying to stop with the affirmation!

That's why I developed Refuturing Statements instead. Refuturing Statements start out with the phrase "What if it's possible." Your mind can't argue with that because it's always *possible*. So instead of looking for counter-evidence, your mind relaxes and begins to open up to *possibility*. You begin to expand.

If you see something as impossible, it's not going to happen. The door is closed to it. It also won't happen if part of you believes it can, but another part strongly believes it can't. You end up working against yourself and your dreams. Once you can hold something as a possibility and align all of yourself with it, there's an opening for it to show up in your life.

The more you sit with the possibility, the bigger the possibility becomes. You might find yourself naturally changing from. "What if it's possible this can happen for me" to, "This can happen for me." Just don't rush it. Being with the possibility is powerful in itself.

These are Refuturing Statements rather than Refuturing Questions because they *are* so powerful. My editor asked me about that with the book. Usually when we start with "What if" we're asking a question. Not here. This is a statement of possibility.

You have space on the Processing Pages to create five Refuturing Statements. If you want to create more, go for it. If you want some suggestions, check out the list of them in the Appendix. I highly recommend keeping a list of yours somewhere so that you can read through them regularly. You'll be amazed at what a difference they can make to your outlook, mindset, and vibration level.

Choose Statements

After you've created your Refuturing Statements, there's space for you to create a Choose Statement. This is something you can use as a touchpoint to realign yourself whenever you feel like you're drifting off-course or when you need an energy boost. It might include whatever *aha* you had while processing.

In the chapter called "Lightning Bolts of DUH," I talk about how these statements might seem super obvious from one point of view. For example, of *course* you choose to fully be yourself. Who wouldn't? But what you're doing through this writing and processing is taking that knowing down to a deeper level. You're *experiencing* it, which is a whole different thing from *thinking* it or *believing* it. When you write it down, your mind may say, "Of course I choose this," while the rest of you feels deep shifts and like the sun is coming out.

I've created a whole list of Choose Statements in the Appendix. You can use them or let them inspire you to write something else. The #1 most important thing is that the statement resonates for *you*. It doesn't need to be what anyone else would choose. It doesn't even need to make sense to anyone else. You know what you mean, and if it calls you to more authenticity, expression, and love, then use it.

One recommendation is that you keep the statement positive. Using a negative can reinforce whatever you're talking about. Feel the difference between, "I choose not to get upset and yell when someone cuts me off in traffic" and "I choose to stay relaxed and centered, including when someone cuts me off in traffic."

Again, I strongly recommend keeping your current choose statement (or all of them) where you'll see them often. Some of my clients have kept a list of them on the wall behind their desk. Some create artwork out of them. Some make them the wallpaper on their phone. Get creative and do what works for you.

The Power Pose

If you haven't watched Amy Cuddy's TED talk, "Your body language may shape who you are," or read her book, *Presence*, you might want to do that soon. She's done extensive research that shows that the practice of power posing for several minutes makes a significant and measurable difference in how boldly we live our lives and in the quality of our decision-making, even hours later. If you watch *Grey's Anatomy*, you'll have seen Dr. Amelia Shephard power posing before performing brain surgery and having her team join in.

Power posing means standing or sitting in a position where you take up space. If you're standing, place your feet wide apart and firmly planted on the ground. Your hands can be on your hips (think Wonder Woman or Superman), or held above your head and angled outward (like a starfish). If you're sitting, your hands can be on the back of your head with elbows out, and legs either splayed or with one ankle resting on the opposite knee. Roll your shoulders back and bring your chest forward.

As you hold one of these poses, breathe deeply.

I've found that power posing while saying Refuturing and Choose Statements, and the other statements in the Appendix, cranks up their power tremendously. I feel them resonating throughout my whole body and energy system.

Because I am who I am, I decided to go a notch further by power posing while looking myself in the eyes in a mirror. The first few times I did it, I couldn't do any of the statements. Holding my own gaze in the mirror while power posing was such an intense experience that it was all I could do. The first day, tears came up and I could only do it for a short time. Gradually, the intensity decreased, and I could hold the pose and my gaze for longer periods. I then added in saying the Refuturing and Choose Statements while in the pose at the mirror. This is one of my favorite practices now.

Opening to the Universe

We're always connected to something greater than our individual selves. I refer to it here as the Universe. Other names include God, Spirit, Source, All That Is, the Divine, and many, many more. Whatever name you use, being open to and feeling your connection with it gives you access to something that goes beyond your typical knowing.

As you complete this section, make the intention to open yourself up to that, to the greater knowing. You're not trying to find the right wise answer. You're not trying to get a grand answer to life's mysteries, or shocking wisdom to share with the world. You're simply opening yourself to receive a deeper wisdom that you always have and may not be in the habit of accessing.

If you're new to this, it may feel odd or challenging. If so, try this: Sit quietly, eyes closed, and take a few deep breaths (inhale while counting slowly to four, exhale while counting slowly to four). Imagine yourself in the presence of the Universe (or the name you use). Imagine love flowing from the Universe and filling you. Imagine that with this love comes knowledge and insights. What do you notice? What occurs to you? You might notice a sense of being loved and held. You might have a thought like, "Everything's working out" or "I'm okay." You might see or sense yourself doing something specific. You might have a flash of insight. Whatever it is, write it down without judgment.

As you write, let your imagination run. **It's totally okay if you feel like you're pretending or making it up.** It's okay if it sounds silly or too good to be true. The more you relax and play with this, the more wisdom and flow you'll experience.

If what comes to mind is snarky, sarcastic or harsh, it's likely to be coming from your mind or your fears. That's not how the Universe typically communicates with us. Witness that thought and see what else you notice.

You could get a message that's not exactly what you want to hear, like "It's time to move on." While you may not like it and you might feel scared, you'll still know if it resonates for you as being true.

If you have a thought like, "This is BS" or "I can't do this", use a Refuturing Statement. What if it's possible that I really am connected to something more than I realize. What if it's possible I can do this. What if it's possible I can relax, hold this lightly, and trust I'm getting what I need.

Keep playing with it and just see what happens. The more you practice being open, the easier it'll get.

Your Next Step

From this new, spacious way of being, what do you feel *inspired* to do? This isn't about what you *should* do. "Should" has a heaviness to it, an energy of contraction, and comes from your mind or your fears. You're in the energy of expansion now. From this place, what draws you? What feels energizing? What makes you happy and excited to think about?

Be aware that while you may feel excited and energized by an idea, you may also feel scared by it. That's totally normal. Fear often comes up in the face of expansion. Why wouldn't it? You're about to take on something new, something that's a stretch. Your Safety

Self will naturally send out warnings about what *could* happen. Remember that your Safety Self is basing everything on the past. You're working now in the present and future, and in what's possible for you.

When you come to the question, "What's next?", you might have a big thought like, "It's time to write my book," or "It's time to make a big change." That's fine. Write that down. Then write down your one next step. For example, what's next might be for you to write a book. Your next step could be finding an editor/ writing coach, writing an outline, creating a mock cover so it feels real, or telling someone close to you that you're going to do it.

"Write a book" is like your GPS saying, "Drive to New York." While writing a book or driving to New York may be your goal, to make progress you need to break it down into doable steps.

Be cautious about looking for the *right* next step or the *best* next step. Words like that can create blocks and lead to you being stuck. Any step will get you into motion and will begin building momentum.

Let your curiosity and creativity come into play here. If an idea pops into mind—even if it doesn't seem like a logical move—try writing it down and doing it. Your next step could be to rest or to go for a walk. It might be to meditate or to have a difficult conversation you've been avoiding. When you practice following your intuition, it'll get stronger.

Tips

Don't try to get this right.

There is no right or wrong with this process. You're simply acknowledging what's there and creating a way for your insights to emerge. The more you simply express your thoughts and feelings and do the poses with the intention of just being in the experience, the more easily things will flow.

Don't worry if you don't know which emotion to choose.

Again, this isn't about getting the "right" emotion. Just choose one that catches your eye and resonates more or less with what you're feeling and go from there. Starting *somewhere* is more productive than spending time searching for the "right" place to start.

Explore different emotions.

If you feel stuck in an emotion after having written about it, try writing about one that's very different from it and see what comes up. For instance, if you're still feeling angry, try filling out the page on feeling hopeful.

If you find yourself writing about the same emotion or very similar emotions over and over, try writing about something that feels opposite. If you always pick an energized dense emotion to explore, choose something from the calm category for a change. Try this even if you're consistently upbeat. It could be that you're not acknowledging other feelings because you think you're always *supposed* to be happy. Try exploring what you're livid about. You might uncover some depths that can serve you. When you regularly feel what's real and true for you in each moment, whether it's "good" or "bad," you reach a new level of presence, authenticity, and power.

If you don't have time to do both sides of the page, go ahead and start.

You can do the sections that feel most resonant for you in the moment, or just come back and finish later. Waiting for conditions to be perfect before you start is a great way to stay stuck right where you are.

Write what occurs to you.

Don't leave something out because it's "bad" or wrong to say it, or because you don't really believe it. If it came to mind, then there's some little part of you that had that thought or emotion. Writing it down will acknowledge it and allow it to move on. It's like draining an abscess and letting all the gunk come out. It doesn't commit you to anything, and doesn't make a statement about who you are as a person. *Not* writing it down gives it power, and that doesn't serve you.

I don't know.

I don't know is such an easy answer. For many years, it was my default answer. Then I realized that that was a choice I was making. "I don't know" was letting me skim across the surface of life without getting down into the depths. I did it because it felt safe not to know. It didn't offend or anger anyone. Putting a stake in the ground and saying, "*This* is my answer" felt very risky. Not knowing was also more comfortable than feeling what I had to feel *in order to* know. It wasn't that I was doing this purposefully or maliciously, I simply didn't think I knew, and wasn't sitting with it long enough *to* know.

If you get a writing prompt and think, "I don't know," here are a few suggestions to get to knowing.

1. Write down, "I don't know what to write here" and whatever your next thoughts are. Just keep writing. You'll get to a knowing if you just let yourself be present with whatever's there for you. The chapter "Shit's Getting Real" is a real-time reporting of my hitting a block while writing the book.

2. Ask yourself, "If I did know, what would I write?" then write whatever occurs to you. You might be amazed at what comes out.

3. Ask yourself, "What do I know?" and start there.

Don't try to *make* anything happen.

Tempting as it is, don't try to make yourself have results. Don't try to make yourself let go of your feelings. Don't try to make yourself feel better or believe something new. It may be counterintuitive, but the more you push, the more entrenched you become. Relax, do each step, and just see what happens.

You may not notice anything as you're doing these steps, then all of a sudden realize that you're easily doing things that used to feel really hard or even impossible. One client noticed that she'd written and sent an email in about five minutes after one of our calls, after having struggled with it for weeks.

You may notice that you're smiling more, worrying less, and having more fun. You may notice that other people are smiling at you more and are more fun to be around. You may start sleeping better, breathing more deeply, and enjoying your life more.

Let it happen in its time. Appreciate who and how you are now, be open to having even more of all the things you're enjoying, and keep taking your one next step.

Step away from the electronics.

As you use the Processing Pages, some of your old gunk will come up. That's meant to happen. The thing is, it's going to feel uncomfortable. Did you ever have a twitchy feeling when you were in school that made you want to just get out of your seat and move around? You may feel like that as you do this processing, like you just want to get up for a few minutes and take a break.

In these moments, it'll be really tempting to reach for your phone, or go get a snack, or take a nap, or answer a few quick emails, or check Twitter. If you have notifications turned on, you'll probably be checking them before you realize you've picked up your phone.

Try putting your phone in the other room. With the ringer off. (Did you just gasp?) Close your computer. Give yourself this time to focus and find your own wisdom and insights. Use this time to connect with yourself. It's a wonderful investment of your time and attention.

Of course, if you really need to take a break from the exercises, then do it. I'm not at all saying that you can't. What I *am* saying is that there may be real gold for you if you stick with the process. If you let yourself be uncomfortable *and* keep writing, you'll access something deep in yourself. Write about the discomfort and whatever's coming up. See where you're feeling it in your body. Then move your body. Keep exploring. You can do this.

If you haven't downloaded the free recording that accompanies *The Universe F♥cking Loves Me*, then go to **theuniversefckinglovesme.com/gift** and get it now. Listening to it will help shift your energy and allow you to then go back to the process you were working on with more spaciousness and ease.

Want to share?

I've set up a Facebook page called *The Universe Fcking Loves Me.* There's lots of information there and a link to join a free group called **Own Your Power**. There, you can share your insights from using the journal, ask questions, and join in other conversations. Facebook changes things up from time to time, so if you have any problems, write to **info@ refutureyourlife.com** and we'll help you get connected.

You can also go to **www.refutureyourlife.com** for blog articles, free downloads, and more. You can reach me on the following social media: YouTube (Refuture Your Life), twitter (@RefutureYou), Facebook (RefutureYourLife) Instagram (saraarey).

Processing Pages

Tired

Acknowledge Your Feelings

I feel tired about _____

_____

_____

_____

_____

_____

_____

_____

_____

Do the Heart Center Pose and say: *I accept all of these feelings.*
Or, *What if it's possible for me to accept all of these feelings?*

In my body, I notice _____

_____

_____

Move your body

Do the Energy Hookup.

Do the Heart Center Pose and say: *I accept all of this, and I'm open to new insights
     and to experiencing something else.*

Or, *What if it's possible for me to accept all of this, and to be open to new insights
     and to experiencing something else.*

Get Curious

I feel curious about _____

_____

_____

_____

In my body, I notice _____

_____

_____

Get Creative

Refuturing Statements:

♥ *What if it's possible* _____

♥ *What if it's possible* _____

♥ *What if it's possible* _____

♥ *What if it's possible* _____

♥ *What if it's possible* _____

Do the Heart Center Pose and say your Refuturing Statements aloud.

I choose _____

**Say your Choose Statement several times aloud,
ideally while doing the Power Pose and looking into a mirror.**

When I open to the Universe _____

_____

_____

_____

Get Courageous

What's next? _____

*My **one** next step is to* _____

_____

I'll do it by _____

Do the Heart Center Pose and imagine yourself taking the action you just wrote about.

I feel _____

_____

In my body, I notice _____

_____

Write the action on your calendar. Do the Power Pose and *feel* yourself completing it.

Tired

Acknowledge Your Feelings

I feel tired about _____

_____

_____

_____

_____

_____

_____

_____

_____

_____

Do the Heart Center Pose and say: *I accept all of these feelings.*
Or, *What if it's possible for me to accept all of these feelings?*

In my body, I notice _____

_____

_____

Move your body

Do the Energy Hookup.

Do the Heart Center Pose and say: *I accept all of this, and I'm open to new insights and to experiencing something else.*

Or, *What if it's possible for me to accept all of this, and to be open to new insights and to experiencing something else.*

Get Curious

I feel curious about _____

_____

_____

In my body, I notice _____

_____

_____

Get Creative

Refuturing Statements:

♥ *What if it's possible* _____

♥ *What if it's possible* _____

♥ *What if it's possible* _____

♥ *What if it's possible* _____

♥ *What if it's possible* _____

Do the Heart Center Pose and say your Refuturing Statements aloud.

I choose _____

Say your Choose Statement several times aloud,
ideally while doing the Power Pose and looking into a mirror.

When I open to the Universe _____

_____

_____

_____

Get Courageous

What's next? _____

*My **one** next step is to* _____

_____

_____

I'll do it by _____

Do the Heart Center Pose and imagine yourself taking the action you just wrote about.

I feel _____

_____

In my body, I notice _____

_____

Write the action on your calendar. Do the Power Pose and *feel* yourself completing it.

Scared

Acknowledge Your Feelings

I feel scared about _____

_____

_____

_____

_____

_____

_____

_____

_____

_____

Do the Heart Center Pose and say: *I accept all of these feelings.*
Or, *What if it's possible for me to accept all of these feelings?*

In my body, I notice _____

_____

_____

Move your body

Do the Energy Hookup.

Do the Heart Center Pose and say: *I accept all of this, and I'm open to new insights and to experiencing something else.*

Or, *What if it's possible for me to accept all of this, and to be open to new insights and to experiencing something else.*

Get Curious

I feel curious about _____

_____

_____

In my body, I notice _____

_____

_____

Get Creative

Refuturing Statements:

♥ *What if it's possible* _____

♥ *What if it's possible* _____

♥ *What if it's possible* _____

♥ *What if it's possible* _____

♥ *What if it's possible* _____

Do the Heart Center Pose and say your Refuturing Statements aloud.

I choose _____

Say your Choose Statement several times aloud,
ideally while doing the Power Pose and looking into a mirror.

When I open to the Universe _____

_____

_____

_____

Get Courageous

What's next? _____

*My **one** next step is to* _____

_____

_____

I'll do it by _____

Do the Heart Center Pose and imagine yourself taking the action you just wrote about.

I feel _____

_____

In my body, I notice _____

_____

Write the action on your calendar. Do the Power Pose and *feel* yourself completing it.

Scared

Acknowledge Your Feelings

I feel scared about _____

_____

_____

_____

_____

_____

_____

_____

_____

_____

Do the Heart Center Pose and say: *I accept all of these feelings.*
Or, *What if it's possible for me to accept all of these feelings?*

In my body, I notice _____

_____

_____

_____

Move your body

Do the Energy Hookup.

Do the Heart Center Pose and say: *I accept all of this, and I'm open to new insights
     and to experiencing something else.*

Or, *What if it's possible for me to accept all of this, and to be open to new insights
     and to experiencing something else.*

Get Curious

I feel curious about _____

_____

_____

_____

In my body, I notice _____

_____

_____

Get Creative

Refuturing Statements:

♥ *What if it's possible* _____

♥ *What if it's possible* _____

♥ *What if it's possible* _____

♥ *What if it's possible* _____

♥ *What if it's possible* _____

Do the Heart Center Pose and say your Refuturing Statements aloud.

I choose _____

**Say your Choose Statement several times aloud,
ideally while doing the Power Pose and looking into a mirror.**

When I open to the Universe _____

_____

_____

_____

Get Courageous

What's next? _____

*My **one** next step is to* _____

_____

_____

I'll do it by _____

Do the Heart Center Pose and imagine yourself taking the action you just wrote about.

I feel _____

_____

In my body, I notice _____

_____

Write the action on your calendar. Do the Power Pose and *feel* yourself completing it.

Worried

Acknowledge Your Feelings

I feel worried about _____

_____

_____

_____

_____

_____

_____

_____

_____

_____

Do the Heart Center Pose and say: *I accept all of these feelings.*
Or, *What if it's possible for me to accept all of these feelings?*

In my body, I notice _____

_____

_____

Move your body

Do the Energy Hookup.

Do the Heart Center Pose and say: *I accept all of this, and I'm open to new insights
    and to experiencing something else.*

Or, *What if it's possible for me to accept all of this, and to be open to new insights
    and to experiencing something else.*

Get Curious

I feel curious about _____

_____

_____

In my body, I notice _____

_____

_____

Get Creative

Refuturing Statements:

♥ *What if it's possible* _____

♥ *What if it's possible* _____

♥ *What if it's possible* _____

♥ *What if it's possible* _____

♥ *What if it's possible* _____

Do the Heart Center Pose and say your Refuturing Statements aloud.

I choose _____

**Say your Choose Statement several times aloud,
ideally while doing the Power Pose and looking into a mirror.**

When I open to the Universe _____

_____

_____

_____

Get Courageous

What's next? _____

*My **one** next step is to* _____

_____

I'll do it by _____

Do the Heart Center Pose and imagine yourself taking the action you just wrote about.

I feel _____

_____

In my body, I notice _____

Write the action on your calendar. Do the Power Pose and *feel* yourself completing it.

Worried

Acknowledge Your Feelings

I feel worried about _____

_____

_____

_____

_____

_____

_____

_____

_____

Do the Heart Center Pose and say: *I accept all of these feelings.*
Or, *What if it's possible for me to accept all of these feelings?*

In my body, I notice _____

_____

_____

Move your body

Do the Energy Hookup.

Do the Heart Center Pose and say: *I accept all of this, and I'm open to new insights and to experiencing something else.*

Or, *What if it's possible for me to accept all of this, and to be open to new insights and to experiencing something else.*

Get Curious

I feel curious about _____

_____

_____

In my body, I notice _____

_____

_____

Get Creative

Refuturing Statements:

♥ *What if it's possible* _____

♥ *What if it's possible* _____

♥ *What if it's possible* _____

♥ *What if it's possible* _____

♥ *What if it's possible* _____

Do the Heart Center Pose and say your Refuturing Statements aloud.

I choose _____

Say your Choose Statement several times aloud,
ideally while doing the Power Pose and looking into a mirror.

When I open to the Universe _____

_____

_____

_____

Get Courageous

What's next? _____

*My **one** next step is to* _____

_____

I'll do it by _____

Do the Heart Center Pose and imagine yourself taking the action you just wrote about.

I feel _____

_____

In my body, I notice _____

_____

Write the action on your calendar. Do the Power Pose and *feel* yourself completing it.

Frustrated

Acknowledge Your Feelings

I feel frustrated about _____
_____
_____
_____
_____
_____
_____
_____
_____

Do the Heart Center Pose and say: *I accept all of these feelings.*
Or, *What if it's possible for me to accept all of these feelings?*

In my body, I notice _____
_____
_____

Move your body

Do the Energy Hookup.

Do the Heart Center Pose and say: *I accept all of this, and I'm open to new insights and to experiencing something else.*

Or, *What if it's possible for me to accept all of this, and to be open to new insights and to experiencing something else.*

Get Curious

I feel curious about _____
_____
_____
_____

In my body, I notice _____
_____
_____

Get Creative

Refuturing Statements:

♥ *What if it's possible* _____

♥ *What if it's possible* _____

♥ *What if it's possible* _____

♥ *What if it's possible* _____

♥ *What if it's possible* _____

Do the Heart Center Pose and say your Refuturing Statements aloud.

I choose _____

**Say your Choose Statement several times aloud,
ideally while doing the Power Pose and looking into a mirror.**

When I open to the Universe _____

_____

_____

_____

Get Courageous

What's next? _____

*My **one** next step is to* _____

_____

_____

I'll do it by _____

Do the Heart Center Pose and imagine yourself taking the action you just wrote about.

I feel _____

_____

In my body, I notice _____

_____

Write the action on your calendar. Do the Power Pose and *feel* yourself completing it.

Frustrated

Acknowledge Your Feelings

I feel frustrated about _____

_____

_____

_____

_____

_____

_____

_____

_____

Do the Heart Center Pose and say: *I accept all of these feelings.*
Or, *What if it's possible for me to accept all of these feelings?*

In my body, I notice _____

_____

_____

Move your body

Do the Energy Hookup.

Do the Heart Center Pose and say: *I accept all of this, and I'm open to new insights*
and to experiencing something else.

Or, *What if it's possible for me to accept all of this, and to be open to new insights*
and to experiencing something else.

Get Curious

I feel curious about _____

_____

_____

In my body, I notice _____

_____

_____

Get Creative

Refuturing Statements:

♥ *What if it's possible* _____

♥ *What if it's possible* _____

♥ *What if it's possible* _____

♥ *What if it's possible* _____

♥ *What if it's possible* _____

Do the Heart Center Pose and say your Refuturing Statements aloud.

I choose _____

**Say your Choose Statement several times aloud,
ideally while doing the Power Pose and looking into a mirror.**

When I open to the Universe _____

_____

_____

_____

Get Courageous

What's next? _____

*My **one** next step is to* _____

_____

I'll do it by _____

Do the Heart Center Pose and imagine yourself taking the action you just wrote about.

I feel _____

In my body, I notice _____

Write the action on your calendar. Do the Power Pose and *feel* yourself completing it.

Hurt

Acknowledge Your Feelings

I feel hurt about _____

_____

_____

_____

_____

_____

_____

_____

_____

_____

Do the Heart Center Pose and say: *I accept all of these feelings.*
Or, *What if it's possible for me to accept all of these feelings?*

In my body, I notice _____

_____

_____

Move your body

Do the Energy Hookup.

Do the Heart Center Pose and say: *I accept all of this, and I'm open to new insights and to experiencing something else.*

Or, *What if it's possible for me to accept all of this, and to be open to new insights and to experiencing something else.*

Get Curious

I feel curious about _____

_____

_____

In my body, I notice _____

_____

_____

Get Creative

Refuturing Statements:

♥ *What if it's possible* _____

♥ *What if it's possible* _____

♥ *What if it's possible* _____

♥ *What if it's possible* _____

♥ *What if it's possible* _____

Do the Heart Center Pose and say your Refuturing Statements aloud.

I choose _____

**Say your Choose Statement several times aloud,
ideally while doing the Power Pose and looking into a mirror.**

When I open to the Universe _____

_____

_____

_____

Get Courageous

What's next? _____

*My **one** next step is to* _____

_____

_____

I'll do it by _____

Do the Heart Center Pose and imagine yourself taking the action you just wrote about.

I feel _____

_____

In my body, I notice _____

_____

Write the action on your calendar. Do the Power Pose and *feel* yourself completing it.

Hurt

Acknowledge Your Feelings

I feel hurt about _____

_____

_____

_____

_____

_____

_____

_____

_____

_____

Do the Heart Center Pose and say: *I accept all of these feelings.*
Or, *What if it's possible for me to accept all of these feelings?*

In my body, I notice _____

_____

_____

Move your body

Do the Energy Hookup.

Do the Heart Center Pose and say: *I accept all of this, and I'm open to new insights and to experiencing something else.*

Or, *What if it's possible for me to accept all of this, and to be open to new insights and to experiencing something else.*

Get Curious

I feel curious about _____

_____

_____

In my body, I notice _____

_____

_____

Get Creative

Refuturing Statements:

♥ *What if it's possible* _____

♥ *What if it's possible* _____

♥ *What if it's possible* _____

♥ *What if it's possible* _____

♥ *What if it's possible* _____

Do the Heart Center Pose and say your Refuturing Statements aloud.

I choose _____

**Say your Choose Statement several times aloud,
ideally while doing the Power Pose and looking into a mirror.**

When I open to the Universe _____

_____

_____

_____

Get Courageous

What's next? _____

*My **one** next step is to* _____

_____

_____

I'll do it by _____

Do the Heart Center Pose and imagine yourself taking the action you just wrote about.

I feel _____

_____

In my body, I notice _____

_____

Write the action on your calendar. Do the Power Pose and *feel* yourself completing it.

Sad

Acknowledge Your Feelings

I feel sad about _____
_____
_____
_____
_____
_____
_____
_____
_____
_____

Do the Heart Center Pose and say: *I accept all of these feelings.*
Or, *What if it's possible for me to accept all of these feelings?*

In my body, I notice _____
_____
_____

Move your body

Do the Energy Hookup.

Do the Heart Center Pose and say: *I accept all of this, and I'm open to new insights
and to experiencing something else.*

Or, *What if it's possible for me to accept all of this, and to be open to new insights
and to experiencing something else.*

Get Curious

I feel curious about _____
_____
_____

In my body, I notice _____
_____
_____

Get Creative

Refuturing Statements:

♥ *What if it's possible* _____

♥ *What if it's possible* _____

♥ *What if it's possible* _____

♥ *What if it's possible* _____

♥ *What if it's possible* _____

Do the Heart Center Pose and say your Refuturing Statements aloud.

I choose _____

**Say your Choose Statement several times aloud,
ideally while doing the Power Pose and looking into a mirror.**

When I open to the Universe _____

_____

_____

_____

Get Courageous

What's next? _____

*My **one** next step is to* _____

_____

_____

I'll do it by _____

Do the Heart Center Pose and imagine yourself taking the action you just wrote about.

I feel _____

_____

In my body, I notice _____

_____

Write the action on your calendar. Do the Power Pose and *feel* yourself completing it.

Sad

Acknowledge Your Feelings

I feel sad about _____

_____

_____

_____

_____

_____

_____

_____

_____

Do the Heart Center Pose and say: *I accept all of these feelings.*
Or, *What if it's possible for me to accept all of these feelings?*

In my body, I notice _____

_____

_____

Move your body

Do the Energy Hookup.

Do the Heart Center Pose and say: *I accept all of this, and I'm open to new insights
    and to experiencing something else.*

Or, *What if it's possible for me to accept all of this, and to be open to new insights
    and to experiencing something else.*

Get Curious

I feel curious about _____

_____

_____

In my body, I notice _____

_____

_____

Get Creative

Refuturing Statements:

♥ *What if it's possible* _____

♥ *What if it's possible* _____

♥ *What if it's possible* _____

♥ *What if it's possible* _____

♥ *What if it's possible* _____

Do the Heart Center Pose and say your Refuturing Statements aloud.

I choose _____

Say your Choose Statement several times aloud,
ideally while doing the Power Pose and looking into a mirror.

When I open to the Universe _____

_____

_____

_____

Get Courageous

What's next? _____

*My **one** next step is to* _____

_____

I'll do it by _____

Do the Heart Center Pose and imagine yourself taking the action you just wrote about.

I feel _____

_____

In my body, I notice _____

_____

Write the action on your calendar. Do the Power Pose and *feel* yourself completing it.

Lonely

Acknowledge Your Feelings

I feel lonely about _____

_____

_____

_____

_____

_____

_____

_____

_____

_____

Do the Heart Center Pose and say: *I accept all of these feelings.*
Or, *What if it's possible for me to accept all of these feelings?*

In my body, I notice _____

_____

_____

Move your body

Do the Energy Hookup.

Do the Heart Center Pose and say: *I accept all of this, and I'm open to new insights and to experiencing something else.*

Or, *What if it's possible for me to accept all of this, and to be open to new insights and to experiencing something else.*

Get Curious

I feel curious about _____

_____

_____

_____

In my body, I notice _____

_____

_____

Get Creative

Refuturing Statements:

♥ *What if it's possible* _____

♥ *What if it's possible* _____

♥ *What if it's possible* _____

♥ *What if it's possible* _____

♥ *What if it's possible* _____

Do the Heart Center Pose and say your Refuturing Statements aloud.

I choose _____

Say your Choose Statement several times aloud,
ideally while doing the Power Pose and looking into a mirror.

When I open to the Universe _____

_____

_____

_____

Get Courageous

What's next? _____

*My **one** next step is to* _____

_____

_____

I'll do it by _____

Do the Heart Center Pose and imagine yourself taking the action you just wrote about.

I feel _____

_____

In my body, I notice _____

_____

Write the action on your calendar. Do the Power Pose and *feel* yourself completing it.

Lonely

Acknowledge Your Feelings

I feel lonely about _____

_____

_____

_____

_____

_____

_____

_____

Do the Heart Center Pose and say: *I accept all of these feelings.*
Or, *What if it's possible for me to accept all of these feelings?*

In my body, I notice _____

_____

_____

Move your body

Do the Energy Hookup.

Do the Heart Center Pose and say: *I accept all of this, and I'm open to new insights
and to experiencing something else.*

Or, *What if it's possible for me to accept all of this, and to be open to new insights
and to experiencing something else.*

Get Curious

I feel curious about _____

_____

_____

In my body, I notice _____

_____

_____

Get Creative

Refuturing Statements:

♥ *What if it's possible* _____

♥ *What if it's possible* _____

♥ *What if it's possible* _____

♥ *What if it's possible* _____

♥ *What if it's possible* _____

Do the Heart Center Pose and say your Refuturing Statements aloud.

I choose _____

**Say your Choose Statement several times aloud,
ideally while doing the Power Pose and looking into a mirror.**

When I open to the Universe _____

_____

_____

_____

Get Courageous

What's next? _____

*My **one** next step is to* _____

_____

I'll do it by _____

Do the Heart Center Pose and imagine yourself taking the action you just wrote about.

I feel _____

_____

In my body, I notice _____

_____

Write the action on your calendar. Do the Power Pose and *feel* yourself completing it.

Guilty

Acknowledge Your Feelings

I feel guilty about _____

_____

_____

_____

_____

_____

_____

_____

_____

Do the Heart Center Pose and say: *I accept all of these feelings.*
Or, *What if it's possible for me to accept all of these feelings?*

In my body, I notice _____

_____

_____

Move your body

Do the Energy Hookup.

Do the Heart Center Pose and say: *I accept all of this, and I'm open to new insights and to experiencing something else.*

Or, *What if it's possible for me to accept all of this, and to be open to new insights and to experiencing something else.*

Get Curious

I feel curious about _____

_____

_____

In my body, I notice _____

_____

_____

Get Creative

Refuturing Statements:

♥ *What if it's possible* _____

♥ *What if it's possible* _____

♥ *What if it's possible* _____

♥ *What if it's possible* _____

♥ *What if it's possible* _____

Do the Heart Center Pose and say your Refuturing Statements aloud.

I choose _____

**Say your Choose Statement several times aloud,
ideally while doing the Power Pose and looking into a mirror.**

When I open to the Universe _____

_____

_____

_____

Get Courageous

What's next? _____

*My **one** next step is to* _____

_____

_____

I'll do it by _____

Do the Heart Center Pose and imagine yourself taking the action you just wrote about.

I feel _____

_____

In my body, I notice _____

_____

Write the action on your calendar. Do the Power Pose and *feel* yourself completing it.

Guilty

Acknowledge Your Feelings

I feel guilty about _____

_____

_____

_____

_____

_____

_____

_____

_____

Do the Heart Center Pose and say: *I accept all of these feelings.*
Or, *What if it's possible for me to accept all of these feelings?*

In my body, I notice _____

_____

_____

Move your body

Do the Energy Hookup.

Do the Heart Center Pose and say: *I accept all of this, and I'm open to new insights
    and to experiencing something else.*

Or, *What if it's possible for me to accept all of this, and to be open to new insights
    and to experiencing something else.*

Get Curious

I feel curious about _____

_____

_____

_____

In my body, I notice _____

_____

_____

Get Creative

Refuturing Statements:

♥ *What if it's possible* _____

♥ *What if it's possible* _____

♥ *What if it's possible* _____

♥ *What if it's possible* _____

♥ *What if it's possible* _____

Do the Heart Center Pose and say your Refuturing Statements aloud.

I choose _____

**Say your Choose Statement several times aloud,
ideally while doing the Power Pose and looking into a mirror.**

When I open to the Universe _____

_____

_____

_____

Get Courageous

What's next? _____

My **one** *next step is to* _____

_____

I'll do it by _____

Do the Heart Center Pose and imagine yourself taking the action you just wrote about.

I feel _____

_____

In my body, I notice _____

_____

Write the action on your calendar. Do the Power Pose and *feel* yourself completing it.

Hopeless

Acknowledge Your Feelings

I feel hopeless about _____

_____

_____

_____

_____

_____

_____

_____

_____

Do the Heart Center Pose and say: *I accept all of these feelings.*
Or, *What if it's possible for me to accept all of these feelings?*

In my body, I notice _____

_____

_____

Move your body

Do the Energy Hookup.

Do the Heart Center Pose and say: *I accept all of this, and I'm open to new insights
and to experiencing something else.*

Or, *What if it's possible for me to accept all of this, and to be open to new insights
and to experiencing something else.*

Get Curious

I feel curious about _____

_____

_____

_____

In my body, I notice _____

_____

_____

Get Creative

Refuturing Statements:

♥ *What if it's possible* _____

♥ *What if it's possible* _____

♥ *What if it's possible* _____

♥ *What if it's possible* _____

♥ *What if it's possible* _____

Do the Heart Center Pose and say your Refuturing Statements aloud.

I choose _____

**Say your Choose Statement several times aloud,
ideally while doing the Power Pose and looking into a mirror.**

When I open to the Universe _____

_____

_____

_____

Get Courageous

What's next? _____

*My **one** next step is to* _____

_____

I'll do it by _____

Do the Heart Center Pose and imagine yourself taking the action you just wrote about.

I feel _____

_____

In my body, I notice _____

_____

Write the action on your calendar. Do the Power Pose and *feel* yourself completing it.

Hopeless

Acknowledge Your Feelings

I feel hopeless about _____
_____
_____
_____
_____
_____
_____
_____

Do the Heart Center Pose and say: *I accept all of these feelings.*
Or, *What if it's possible for me to accept all of these feelings?*

In my body, I notice _____
_____
_____

Move your body

Do the Energy Hookup.

Do the Heart Center Pose and say: *I accept all of this, and I'm open to new insights and to experiencing something else.*

Or, *What if it's possible for me to accept all of this, and to be open to new insights and to experiencing something else.*

Get Curious

I feel curious about _____
_____
_____
_____

In my body, I notice _____
_____
_____

Get Creative

Refuturing Statements:

♥ *What if it's possible* _____

♥ *What if it's possible* _____

♥ *What if it's possible* _____

♥ *What if it's possible* _____

♥ *What if it's possible* _____

Do the Heart Center Pose and say your Refuturing Statements aloud.

I choose _____

**Say your Choose Statement several times aloud,
ideally while doing the Power Pose and looking into a mirror.**

When I open to the Universe _____

_____

_____

_____

Get Courageous

What's next? _____

*My **one** next step is to* _____

_____

_____

I'll do it by _____

Do the Heart Center Pose and imagine yourself taking the action you just wrote about.

I feel _____

_____

In my body, I notice _____

_____

Write the action on your calendar. Do the Power Pose and *feel* yourself completing it.

Jealous

Acknowledge Your Feelings

I feel jealous about _____

_____

_____

_____

_____

_____

_____

_____

_____

Do the Heart Center Pose and say: *I accept all of these feelings.*
Or, *What if it's possible for me to accept all of these feelings?*

In my body, I notice _____

_____

_____

Move your body

Do the Energy Hookup.

Do the Heart Center Pose and say: *I accept all of this, and I'm open to new insights
and to experiencing something else.*

Or, *What if it's possible for me to accept all of this, and to be open to new insights
and to experiencing something else.*

Get Curious

I feel curious about _____

_____

_____

_____

In my body, I notice _____

_____

_____

Get Creative

Refuturing Statements:

♥ *What if it's possible* _____

♥ *What if it's possible* _____

♥ *What if it's possible* _____

♥ *What if it's possible* _____

♥ *What if it's possible* _____

Do the Heart Center Pose and say your Refuturing Statements aloud.

I choose _____

Say your Choose Statement several times aloud,
ideally while doing the Power Pose and looking into a mirror.

When I open to the Universe _____

_____

_____

_____

Get Courageous

What's next? _____

*My **one** next step is to* _____

_____

_____

I'll do it by _____

Do the Heart Center Pose and imagine yourself taking the action you just wrote about.

I feel _____

_____

In my body, I notice _____

_____

Write the action on your calendar. Do the Power Pose and *feel* yourself completing it.

Jealous

Acknowledge Your Feelings

I feel jealous about _____

_____

_____

_____

_____

_____

_____

_____

_____

Do the Heart Center Pose and say: *I accept all of these feelings.*
Or, *What if it's possible for me to accept all of these feelings?*

In my body, I notice _____

_____

_____

Move your body

Do the Energy Hookup.

Do the Heart Center Pose and say: *I accept all of this, and I'm open to new insights*
    and to experiencing something else.
Or, *What if it's possible for me to accept all of this, and to be open to new insights*
    and to experiencing something else.

Get Curious

I feel curious about _____

_____

_____

In my body, I notice _____

_____

_____

Get Creative

Refuturing Statements:

♥ *What if it's possible* _____

♥ *What if it's possible* _____

♥ *What if it's possible* _____

♥ *What if it's possible* _____

♥ *What if it's possible* _____

Do the Heart Center Pose and say your Refuturing Statements aloud.

I choose _____

Say your Choose Statement several times aloud,
ideally while doing the Power Pose and looking into a mirror.

When I open to the Universe _____

_____

_____

_____

Get Courageous

What's next? _____

*My **one** next step is to* _____

_____

_____

I'll do it by _____

Do the Heart Center Pose and imagine yourself taking the action you just wrote about.

I feel _____

_____

In my body, I notice _____

_____

Write the action on your calendar. Do the Power Pose and *feel* yourself completing it.

Judged

Acknowledge Your Feelings

I feel judged about _____

_____

_____

_____

_____

_____

_____

_____

_____

Do the Heart Center Pose and say: *I accept all of these feelings.*
Or, *What if it's possible for me to accept all of these feelings?*

In my body, I notice _____

_____

_____

Move your body

Do the Energy Hookup.

Do the Heart Center Pose and say: *I accept all of this, and I'm open to new insights*
and to experiencing something else.

Or, *What if it's possible for me to accept all of this, and to be open to new insights*
and to experiencing something else.

Get Curious

I feel curious about _____

_____

_____

In my body, I notice _____

_____

_____

Get Creative

Refuturing Statements:

♥ *What if it's possible* _____

♥ *What if it's possible* _____

♥ *What if it's possible* _____

♥ *What if it's possible* _____

♥ *What if it's possible* _____

Do the Heart Center Pose and say your Refuturing Statements aloud.

I choose _____

**Say your Choose Statement several times aloud,
ideally while doing the Power Pose and looking into a mirror.**

When I open to the Universe _____

_____

_____

_____

Get Courageous

What's next? _____

*My **one** next step is to* _____

_____

I'll do it by _____

Do the Heart Center Pose and imagine yourself taking the action you just wrote about.

I feel _____

_____

In my body, I notice _____

_____

Write the action on your calendar. Do the Power Pose and *feel* yourself completing it.

Judged

Acknowledge Your Feelings

I feel judged about _____

_____

_____

_____

_____

_____

_____

_____

_____

Do the Heart Center Pose and say: *I accept all of these feelings.*
Or, *What if it's possible for me to accept all of these feelings?*

In my body, I notice _____

_____

_____

Move your body

Do the Energy Hookup.

Do the Heart Center Pose and say: *I accept all of this, and I'm open to new insights and to experiencing something else.*

Or, *What if it's possible for me to accept all of this, and to be open to new insights and to experiencing something else.*

Get Curious

I feel curious about _____

_____

_____

In my body, I notice _____

_____

_____

Get Creative

Refuturing Statements:

♥ *What if it's possible* _____

♥ *What if it's possible* _____

♥ *What if it's possible* _____

♥ *What if it's possible* _____

♥ *What if it's possible* _____

Do the Heart Center Pose and say your Refuturing Statements aloud.

I choose _____

Say your Choose Statement several times aloud,
ideally while doing the Power Pose and looking into a mirror.

When I open to the Universe _____

_____

_____

_____

Get Courageous

What's next? _____

*My **one** next step is to* _____

_____

I'll do it by _____

Do the Heart Center Pose and imagine yourself taking the action you just wrote about.

I feel _____

_____

In my body, I notice _____

_____

Write the action on your calendar. Do the Power Pose and *feel* yourself completing it.

Regretful

Acknowledge Your Feelings

I feel regretful about _____

_____

_____

_____

_____

_____

_____

_____

_____

_____

Do the Heart Center Pose and say: *I accept all of these feelings.*
Or, *What if it's possible for me to accept all of these feelings?*

In my body, I notice _____

_____

_____

Move your body

Do the Energy Hookup.

Do the Heart Center Pose and say: *I accept all of this, and I'm open to new insights
    and to experiencing something else.*

Or, *What if it's possible for me to accept all of this, and to be open to new insights
    and to experiencing something else.*

Get Curious

I feel curious about _____

_____

_____

In my body, I notice _____

_____

_____

Get Creative

Refuturing Statements:

♥ *What if it's possible* _____

♥ *What if it's possible* _____

♥ *What if it's possible* _____

♥ *What if it's possible* _____

♥ *What if it's possible* _____

Do the Heart Center Pose and say your Refuturing Statements aloud.

I choose _____

Say your Choose Statement several times aloud,
ideally while doing the Power Pose and looking into a mirror.

When I open to the Universe _____

_____

_____

_____

Get Courageous

What's next? _____

*My **one** next step is to* _____

_____

I'll do it by _____

Do the Heart Center Pose and imagine yourself taking the action you just wrote about.

I feel _____

_____

In my body, I notice _____

_____

Write the action on your calendar. Do the Power Pose and *feel* yourself completing it.

Regretful

Acknowledge Your Feelings

I feel regretful about _____

_____

_____

_____

_____

_____

_____

_____

_____

Do the Heart Center Pose and say: *I accept all of these feelings.*
Or, *What if it's possible for me to accept all of these feelings?*

In my body, I notice _____

_____

_____

Move your body

Do the Energy Hookup.

Do the Heart Center Pose and say: *I accept all of this, and I'm open to new insights and to experiencing something else.*

Or, *What if it's possible for me to accept all of this, and to be open to new insights and to experiencing something else.*

Get Curious

I feel curious about _____

_____

_____

_____

In my body, I notice _____

_____

_____

_____

Get Creative

Refuturing Statements:

♥ *What if it's possible* _____

♥ *What if it's possible* _____

♥ *What if it's possible* _____

♥ *What if it's possible* _____

♥ *What if it's possible* _____

Do the Heart Center Pose and say your Refuturing Statements aloud.

I choose _____

**Say your Choose Statement several times aloud,
ideally while doing the Power Pose and looking into a mirror.**

When I open to the Universe _____

_____

_____

_____

Get Courageous

What's next? _____

*My **one** next step is to* _____

_____

I'll do it by _____

Do the Heart Center Pose and imagine yourself taking the action you just wrote about.

I feel _____

_____

In my body, I notice _____

_____

Write the action on your calendar. Do the Power Pose and *feel* yourself completing it.

Discouraged

Acknowledge Your Feelings

I feel discouraged about _____

_____

_____

_____

_____

_____

_____

_____

_____

Do the Heart Center Pose and say: *I accept all of these feelings.*
Or, *What if it's possible for me to accept all of these feelings?*

In my body, I notice _____

_____

_____

Move your body

Do the Energy Hookup.

Do the Heart Center Pose and say: *I accept all of this, and I'm open to new insights and to experiencing something else.*

Or, *What if it's possible for me to accept all of this, and to be open to new insights and to experiencing something else.*

Get Curious

I feel curious about _____

_____

_____

_____

In my body, I notice _____

_____

_____

Get Creative

Refuturing Statements:

♥ *What if it's possible* _____

♥ *What if it's possible* _____

♥ *What if it's possible* _____

♥ *What if it's possible* _____

♥ *What if it's possible* _____

Do the Heart Center Pose and say your Refuturing Statements aloud.

I choose _____

Say your Choose Statement several times aloud,
ideally while doing the Power Pose and looking into a mirror.

When I open to the Universe _____

_____

_____

_____

Get Courageous

What's next? _____

*My **one** next step is to* _____

_____

I'll do it by _____

Do the Heart Center Pose and imagine yourself taking the action you just wrote about.

I feel _____

_____

In my body, I notice _____

_____

Write the action on your calendar. Do the Power Pose and *feel* yourself completing it.

Discouraged

Acknowledge Your Feelings

I feel discouraged about _____

_____

_____

_____

_____

_____

_____

_____

Do the Heart Center Pose and say: *I accept all of these feelings.*
Or, *What if it's possible for me to accept all of these feelings?*

In my body, I notice _____

_____

_____

Move your body

Do the Energy Hookup.

Do the Heart Center Pose and say: *I accept all of this, and I'm open to new insights and to experiencing something else.*
Or, *What if it's possible for me to accept all of this, and to be open to new insights and to experiencing something else.*

Get Curious

I feel curious about _____

_____

_____

_____

In my body, I notice _____

_____

_____

Get Creative

Refuturing Statements:

♥ *What if it's possible* _____

♥ *What if it's possible* _____

♥ *What if it's possible* _____

♥ *What if it's possible* _____

♥ *What if it's possible* _____

Do the Heart Center Pose and say your Refuturing Statements aloud.

I choose _____

Say your Choose Statement several times aloud,
ideally while doing the Power Pose and looking into a mirror.

When I open to the Universe _____

_____

_____

_____

Get Courageous

What's next? _____

*My **one** next step is to* _____

_____

I'll do it by _____

Do the Heart Center Pose and imagine yourself taking the action you just wrote about.

I feel _____

_____

In my body, I notice _____

_____

Write the action on your calendar. Do the Power Pose and *feel* yourself completing it.

Disappointed

Acknowledge Your Feelings

I feel disappointed about _____

_____

_____

_____

_____

_____

_____

_____

_____

Do the Heart Center Pose and say: *I accept all of these feelings.*
Or, *What if it's possible for me to accept all of these feelings?*

In my body, I notice _____

_____

_____

Move your body

Do the Energy Hookup.

Do the Heart Center Pose and say: *I accept all of this, and I'm open to new insights
    and to experiencing something else.*

Or, *What if it's possible for me to accept all of this, and to be open to new insights
    and to experiencing something else.*

Get Curious

I feel curious about _____

_____

_____

_____

In my body, I notice _____

_____

_____

Get Creative

Refuturing Statements:

♥ *What if it's possible* _____

♥ *What if it's possible* _____

♥ *What if it's possible* _____

♥ *What if it's possible* _____

♥ *What if it's possible* _____

Do the Heart Center Pose and say your Refuturing Statements aloud.

I choose _____

Say your Choose Statement several times aloud,
ideally while doing the Power Pose and looking into a mirror.

When I open to the Universe _____

_____

_____

_____

Get Courageous

What's next? _____

*My **one** next step is to* _____

_____

I'll do it by _____

Do the Heart Center Pose and imagine yourself taking the action you just wrote about.

I feel _____

_____

In my body, I notice _____

_____

Write the action on your calendar. Do the Power Pose and *feel* yourself completing it.

Disappointed

Acknowledge Your Feelings

I feel disappointed about _____
_____
_____
_____
_____
_____
_____
_____
_____
_____

Do the Heart Center Pose and say: *I accept all of these feelings.*
Or, *What if it's possible for me to accept all of these feelings?*

In my body, I notice _____
_____
_____

Move your body

Do the Energy Hookup.

Do the Heart Center Pose and say: *I accept all of this, and I'm open to new insights
    and to experiencing something else.*
Or, *What if it's possible for me to accept all of this, and to be open to new insights
    and to experiencing something else.*

Get Curious

I feel curious about _____
_____
_____

In my body, I notice _____
_____
_____

Get Creative

Refuturing Statements:

♥ *What if it's possible* _____

♥ *What if it's possible* _____

♥ *What if it's possible* _____

♥ *What if it's possible* _____

♥ *What if it's possible* _____

Do the Heart Center Pose and say your Refuturing Statements aloud.

I choose _____

**Say your Choose Statement several times aloud,
ideally while doing the Power Pose and looking into a mirror.**

When I open to the Universe _____

_____

_____

_____

Get Courageous

What's next? _____

*My **one** next step is to* _____

_____

I'll do it by _____

Do the Heart Center Pose and imagine yourself taking the action you just wrote about.

I feel _____

_____

In my body, I notice _____

_____

Write the action on your calendar. Do the Power Pose and *feel* yourself completing it.

Disconnected

Acknowledge Your Feelings

I feel disconnected about _____

_____

_____

_____

_____

_____

_____

_____

_____

Do the Heart Center Pose and say: *I accept all of these feelings.*
Or, *What if it's possible for me to accept all of these feelings?*

In my body, I notice _____

_____

_____

Move your body

Do the Energy Hookup.

Do the Heart Center Pose and say: *I accept all of this, and I'm open to new insights
     and to experiencing something else.*

Or, *What if it's possible for me to accept all of this, and to be open to new insights
     and to experiencing something else.*

Get Curious

I feel curious about _____

_____

_____

In my body, I notice _____

_____

_____

Get Creative

Refuturing Statements:

♥ *What if it's possible* _____

♥ *What if it's possible* _____

♥ *What if it's possible* _____

♥ *What if it's possible* _____

♥ *What if it's possible* _____

Do the Heart Center Pose and say your Refuturing Statements aloud.

I choose _____

**Say your Choose Statement several times aloud,
ideally while doing the Power Pose and looking into a mirror.**

When I open to the Universe _____

_____

_____

_____

Get Courageous

What's next? _____

*My **one** next step is to* _____

_____

I'll do it by _____

Do the Heart Center Pose and imagine yourself taking the action you just wrote about.

I feel _____

_____

In my body, I notice _____

_____

Write the action on your calendar. Do the Power Pose and *feel* yourself completing it.

Disconnected

Acknowledge Your Feelings

I feel disconnected about _____

_____

_____

_____

_____

_____

_____

_____

_____

Do the Heart Center Pose and say: *I accept all of these feelings.*
Or, *What if it's possible for me to accept all of these feelings?*

In my body, I notice _____

_____

_____

Move your body

Do the Energy Hookup.

Do the Heart Center Pose and say: *I accept all of this, and I'm open to new insights
    and to experiencing something else.*

Or, *What if it's possible for me to accept all of this, and to be open to new insights
    and to experiencing something else.*

Get Curious

I feel curious about _____

_____

_____

_____

In my body, I notice _____

_____

_____

Get Creative

Refuturing Statements:

♥ *What if it's possible* _____

♥ *What if it's possible* _____

♥ *What if it's possible* _____

♥ *What if it's possible* _____

♥ *What if it's possible* _____

Do the Heart Center Pose and say your Refuturing Statements aloud.

I choose _____

Say your Choose Statement several times aloud,
ideally while doing the Power Pose and looking into a mirror.

When I open to the Universe _____

_____

_____

_____

Get Courageous

What's next? _____

*My **one** next step is to* _____

_____

_____

I'll do it by _____

Do the Heart Center Pose and imagine yourself taking the action you just wrote about.

I feel _____

_____

In my body, I notice _____

_____

Write the action on your calendar. Do the Power Pose and *feel* yourself completing it.

Angry

Acknowledge Your Feelings

I feel angry about _____

_____

_____

_____

_____

_____

_____

_____

_____

_____

Do the Heart Center Pose and say: *I accept all of these feelings.*
Or, *What if it's possible for me to accept all of these feelings?*

In my body, I notice _____

_____

_____

Move your body

Do the Energy Hookup.

Do the Heart Center Pose and say: *I accept all of this, and I'm open to new insights and to experiencing something else.*

Or, *What if it's possible for me to accept all of this, and to be open to new insights and to experiencing something else.*

Get Curious

I feel curious about _____

_____

_____

_____

In my body, I notice _____

_____

_____

Get Creative

Refuturing Statements:

♥ *What if it's possible* _____

♥ *What if it's possible* _____

♥ *What if it's possible* _____

♥ *What if it's possible* _____

♥ *What if it's possible* _____

Do the Heart Center Pose and say your Refuturing Statements aloud.

I choose _____

**Say your Choose Statement several times aloud,
ideally while doing the Power Pose and looking into a mirror.**

When I open to the Universe _____

_____

_____

_____

Get Courageous

What's next? _____

*My **one** next step is to* _____

_____

I'll do it by _____

Do the Heart Center Pose and imagine yourself taking the action you just wrote about.

I feel _____

_____

In my body, I notice _____

_____

Write the action on your calendar. Do the Power Pose and *feel* yourself completing it.

Angry

Acknowledge Your Feelings

I feel angry about _____

_____

_____

_____

_____

_____

_____

_____

_____

Do the Heart Center Pose and say: *I accept all of these feelings.*
Or, *What if it's possible for me to accept all of these feelings?*

In my body, I notice _____

_____

_____

Move your body

Do the Energy Hookup.

Do the Heart Center Pose and say: *I accept all of this, and I'm open to new insights and to experiencing something else.*

Or, *What if it's possible for me to accept all of this, and to be open to new insights and to experiencing something else.*

Get Curious

I feel curious about _____

_____

_____

_____

In my body, I notice _____

_____

_____

Get Creative

Refuturing Statements:

♥ *What if it's possible* _____

♥ *What if it's possible* _____

♥ *What if it's possible* _____

♥ *What if it's possible* _____

♥ *What if it's possible* _____

Do the Heart Center Pose and say your Refuturing Statements aloud.

I choose _____

Say your Choose Statement several times aloud,
ideally while doing the Power Pose and looking into a mirror.

When I open to the Universe _____

_____

_____

_____

Get Courageous

What's next? _____

*My **one** next step is to* _____

_____

_____

I'll do it by _____

Do the Heart Center Pose and imagine yourself taking the action you just wrote about.

I feel _____

_____

In my body, I notice _____

_____

Write the action on your calendar. Do the Power Pose and *feel* yourself completing it.

Embarrassed

Acknowledge Your Feelings

I feel embarrassed about _____

_____

_____

_____

_____

_____

_____

_____

_____

_____

Do the Heart Center Pose and say: *I accept all of these feelings.*
Or, *What if it's possible for me to accept all of these feelings?*

In my body, I notice _____

_____

_____

Move your body

Do the Energy Hookup.

Do the Heart Center Pose and say: *I accept all of this, and I'm open to new insights and to experiencing something else.*

Or, *What if it's possible for me to accept all of this, and to be open to new insights and to experiencing something else.*

Get Curious

I feel curious about _____

_____

_____

_____

In my body, I notice _____

_____

_____

Get Creative

Refuturing Statements:

♥ *What if it's possible* _____

♥ *What if it's possible* _____

♥ *What if it's possible* _____

♥ *What if it's possible* _____

♥ *What if it's possible* _____

Do the Heart Center Pose and say your Refuturing Statements aloud.

I choose _____

**Say your Choose Statement several times aloud,
ideally while doing the Power Pose and looking into a mirror.**

When I open to the Universe _____

_____

_____

_____

Get Courageous

What's next? _____

*My **one** next step is to* _____

_____

_____

I'll do it by _____

Do the Heart Center Pose and imagine yourself taking the action you just wrote about.

I feel _____

_____

In my body, I notice _____

_____

Write the action on your calendar. Do the Power Pose and *feel* yourself completing it.

Embarrassed

Acknowledge Your Feelings

I feel embarrassed about _____

_____

_____

_____

_____

_____

_____

_____

_____

_____

Do the Heart Center Pose and say: *I accept all of these feelings.*
Or, *What if it's possible for me to accept all of these feelings?*

In my body, I notice _____

_____

_____

Move your body

Do the Energy Hookup.

Do the Heart Center Pose and say: *I accept all of this, and I'm open to new insights and to experiencing something else.*

Or, *What if it's possible for me to accept all of this, and to be open to new insights and to experiencing something else.*

Get Curious

I feel curious about _____

_____

_____

In my body, I notice _____

_____

_____

Get Creative

Refuturing Statements:

♥ *What if it's possible* _____

♥ *What if it's possible* _____

♥ *What if it's possible* _____

♥ *What if it's possible* _____

♥ *What if it's possible* _____

Do the Heart Center Pose and say your Refuturing Statements aloud.

I choose _____

Say your Choose Statement several times aloud,
ideally while doing the Power Pose and looking into a mirror.

When I open to the Universe _____

_____

_____

_____

Get Courageous

What's next? _____

*My **one** next step is to* _____

_____

_____

I'll do it by _____

Do the Heart Center Pose and imagine yourself taking the action you just wrote about.

I feel _____

_____

In my body, I notice _____

_____

Write the action on your calendar. Do the Power Pose and *feel* yourself completing it.

Ashamed

Acknowledge Your Feelings

I feel ashamed about _____
_____
_____
_____
_____
_____
_____
_____
_____

Do the Heart Center Pose and say: *I accept all of these feelings.*
Or, *What if it's possible for me to accept all of these feelings?*

In my body, I notice _____
_____
_____

Move your body

Do the Energy Hookup.

Do the Heart Center Pose and say: *I accept all of this, and I'm open to new insights and to experiencing something else.*

Or, *What if it's possible for me to accept all of this, and to be open to new insights and to experiencing something else.*

Get Curious

I feel curious about _____
_____
_____
_____

In my body, I notice _____
_____
_____

Get Creative

Refuturing Statements:

♥ *What if it's possible* _____

♥ *What if it's possible* _____

♥ *What if it's possible* _____

♥ *What if it's possible* _____

♥ *What if it's possible* _____

Do the Heart Center Pose and say your Refuturing Statements aloud.

I choose _____

**Say your Choose Statement several times aloud,
ideally while doing the Power Pose and looking into a mirror.**

When I open to the Universe _____

_____

_____

_____

Get Courageous

What's next? _____

*My **one** next step is to* _____

_____

_____

I'll do it by _____

Do the Heart Center Pose and imagine yourself taking the action you just wrote about.

I feel _____

_____

In my body, I notice _____

_____

Write the action on your calendar. Do the Power Pose and *feel* yourself completing it.

Ashamed

Acknowledge Your Feelings

I feel ashamed about _____

_____

_____

_____

_____

_____

_____

_____

Do the Heart Center Pose and say: *I accept all of these feelings.*
Or, *What if it's possible for me to accept all of these feelings?*

In my body, I notice _____

_____

_____

Move your body

Do the Energy Hookup.

Do the Heart Center Pose and say: *I accept all of this, and I'm open to new insights*
   and to experiencing something else.

Or, *What if it's possible for me to accept all of this, and to be open to new insights*
   and to experiencing something else.

Get Curious

I feel curious about _____

_____

_____

In my body, I notice _____

_____

_____

Get Creative

Refuturing Statements:

♥ *What if it's possible* _____

♥ *What if it's possible* _____

♥ *What if it's possible* _____

♥ *What if it's possible* _____

♥ *What if it's possible* _____

Do the Heart Center Pose and say your Refuturing Statements aloud.

I choose _____

Say your Choose Statement several times aloud,
ideally while doing the Power Pose and looking into a mirror.

When I open to the Universe _____

_____

_____

_____

Get Courageous

What's next? _____

*My **one** next step is to* _____

_____

_____

I'll do it by _____

Do the Heart Center Pose and imagine yourself taking the action you just wrote about.

I feel _____

_____

In my body, I notice _____

_____

Write the action on your calendar. Do the Power Pose and *feel* yourself completing it.

Resentful

Acknowledge Your Feelings

I feel resentful about _____
_____
_____
_____
_____
_____
_____
_____
_____

Do the Heart Center Pose and say: *I accept all of these feelings.*
Or, *What if it's possible for me to accept all of these feelings?*

In my body, I notice _____
_____
_____

Move your body

Do the Energy Hookup.

Do the Heart Center Pose and say: *I accept all of this, and I'm open to new insights
   and to experiencing something else.*

Or, *What if it's possible for me to accept all of this, and to be open to new insights
   and to experiencing something else.*

Get Curious

I feel curious about _____
_____
_____
_____

In my body, I notice _____
_____
_____

Get Creative

Refuturing Statements:

♥ *What if it's possible* _____

♥ *What if it's possible* _____

♥ *What if it's possible* _____

♥ *What if it's possible* _____

♥ *What if it's possible* _____

Do the Heart Center Pose and say your Refuturing Statements aloud.

I choose _____

**Say your Choose Statement several times aloud,
ideally while doing the Power Pose and looking into a mirror.**

When I open to the Universe _____

_____

_____

_____

Get Courageous

What's next? _____

My **one** *next step is to* _____

_____

I'll do it by _____

Do the Heart Center Pose and imagine yourself taking the action you just wrote about.

I feel _____

_____

In my body, I notice _____

_____

Write the action on your calendar. Do the Power Pose and *feel* yourself completing it.

Resentful

Acknowledge Your Feelings

I feel resentful about _____
_____
_____
_____
_____
_____
_____
_____
_____
_____

Do the Heart Center Pose and say: *I accept all of these feelings.*
Or, *What if it's possible for me to accept all of these feelings?*

In my body, I notice _____
_____
_____

Move your body

Do the Energy Hookup.

Do the Heart Center Pose and say: *I accept all of this, and I'm open to new insights and to experiencing something else.*

Or, *What if it's possible for me to accept all of this, and to be open to new insights and to experiencing something else.*

Get Curious

I feel curious about _____
_____
_____
_____

In my body, I notice _____
_____
_____

Get Creative

Refuturing Statements:

♥ *What if it's possible* _____

♥ *What if it's possible* _____

♥ *What if it's possible* _____

♥ *What if it's possible* _____

♥ *What if it's possible* _____

Do the Heart Center Pose and say your Refuturing Statements aloud.

I choose _____

**Say your Choose Statement several times aloud,
ideally while doing the Power Pose and looking into a mirror.**

When I open to the Universe _____

_____

_____

_____

Get Courageous

What's next? _____

*My **one** next step is to* _____

_____

_____

I'll do it by _____

Do the Heart Center Pose and imagine yourself taking the action you just wrote about.

I feel _____

_____

In my body, I notice _____

_____

Write the action on your calendar. Do the Power Pose and *feel* yourself completing it.

Uncomfortable

Acknowledge Your Feelings

I feel uncomfortable about _____

_____

_____

_____

_____

_____

_____

_____

_____

Do the Heart Center Pose and say: *I accept all of these feelings.*
Or, *What if it's possible for me to accept all of these feelings?*

In my body, I notice _____

_____

_____

Move your body

Do the Energy Hookup.

Do the Heart Center Pose and say: *I accept all of this, and I'm open to new insights and to experiencing something else.*

Or, *What if it's possible for me to accept all of this, and to be open to new insights and to experiencing something else.*

Get Curious

I feel curious about _____

_____

_____

_____

In my body, I notice _____

_____

_____

Get Creative

Refuturing Statements:

♥ *What if it's possible* _____

♥ *What if it's possible* _____

♥ *What if it's possible* _____

♥ *What if it's possible* _____

♥ *What if it's possible* _____

Do the Heart Center Pose and say your Refuturing Statements aloud.

I choose _____

Say your Choose Statement several times aloud,
ideally while doing the Power Pose and looking into a mirror.

When I open to the Universe _____

_____

_____

_____

Get Courageous

What's next? _____

*My **one** next step is to* _____

_____

_____

I'll do it by _____

Do the Heart Center Pose and imagine yourself taking the action you just wrote about.

I feel _____

_____

In my body, I notice _____

_____

Write the action on your calendar. Do the Power Pose and *feel* yourself completing it.

Uncomfortable

Acknowledge Your Feelings

I feel uncomfortable about _____

_____

_____

_____

_____

_____

_____

_____

_____

_____

Do the Heart Center Pose and say: *I accept all of these feelings.*
Or, *What if it's possible for me to accept all of these feelings?*

In my body, I notice _____

_____

_____

Move your body

Do the Energy Hookup.

Do the Heart Center Pose and say: *I accept all of this, and I'm open to new insights
and to experiencing something else.*

Or, *What if it's possible for me to accept all of this, and to be open to new insights
and to experiencing something else.*

Get Curious

I feel curious about _____

_____

_____

In my body, I notice _____

_____

_____

Get Creative

Refuturing Statements:

♥ *What if it's possible* _____

♥ *What if it's possible* _____

♥ *What if it's possible* _____

♥ *What if it's possible* _____

♥ *What if it's possible* _____

Do the Heart Center Pose and say your Refuturing Statements aloud.

I choose _____

**Say your Choose Statement several times aloud,
ideally while doing the Power Pose and looking into a mirror.**

When I open to the Universe _____

_____

_____

_____

Get Courageous

What's next? _____

*My **one** next step is to* _____

_____

I'll do it by _____

Do the Heart Center Pose and imagine yourself taking the action you just wrote about.

I feel _____

_____

In my body, I notice _____

_____

Write the action on your calendar. Do the Power Pose and *feel* yourself completing it.

Livid

Acknowledge Your Feelings

I feel livid about _____

_____

_____

_____

_____

_____

_____

_____

_____

Do the Heart Center Pose and say: *I accept all of these feelings.*
Or, *What if it's possible for me to accept all of these feelings?*

In my body, I notice _____

_____

_____

Move your body

Do the Energy Hookup.

Do the Heart Center Pose and say: *I accept all of this, and I'm open to new insights and to experiencing something else.*

Or, *What if it's possible for me to accept all of this, and to be open to new insights and to experiencing something else.*

Get Curious

I feel curious about _____

_____

_____

In my body, I notice _____

_____

_____

Get Creative

Refuturing Statements:

♥ *What if it's possible* _____

♥ *What if it's possible* _____

♥ *What if it's possible* _____

♥ *What if it's possible* _____

♥ *What if it's possible* _____

Do the Heart Center Pose and say your Refuturing Statements aloud.

I choose _____

**Say your Choose Statement several times aloud,
ideally while doing the Power Pose and looking into a mirror.**

When I open to the Universe _____

_____

_____

_____

Get Courageous

What's next? _____

*My **one** next step is to* _____

_____

_____

I'll do it by _____

Do the Heart Center Pose and imagine yourself taking the action you just wrote about.

I feel _____

_____

In my body, I notice _____

_____

Write the action on your calendar. Do the Power Pose and *feel* yourself completing it.

Livid

Acknowledge Your Feelings

I feel livid about _____

_____

_____

_____

_____

_____

_____

_____

_____

_____

Do the Heart Center Pose and say: *I accept all of these feelings.*
Or, *What if it's possible for me to accept all of these feelings?*

In my body, I notice _____

_____

_____

Move your body

Do the Energy Hookup.

Do the Heart Center Pose and say: *I accept all of this, and I'm open to new insights
    and to experiencing something else.*

Or, *What if it's possible for me to accept all of this, and to be open to new insights
    and to experiencing something else.*

Get Curious

I feel curious about _____

_____

_____

In my body, I notice _____

_____

_____

Get Creative

Refuturing Statements:

♥ *What if it's possible* _____

♥ *What if it's possible* _____

♥ *What if it's possible* _____

♥ *What if it's possible* _____

♥ *What if it's possible* _____

Do the Heart Center Pose and say your Refuturing Statements aloud.

I choose _____

**Say your Choose Statement several times aloud,
ideally while doing the Power Pose and looking into a mirror.**

When I open to the Universe _____

_____

_____

_____

Get Courageous

What's next? _____

*My **one** next step is to* _____

_____

I'll do it by _____

Do the Heart Center Pose and imagine yourself taking the action you just wrote about.

I feel _____

_____

In my body, I notice _____

_____

Write the action on your calendar. Do the Power Pose and *feel* yourself completing it.

Irritated

Acknowledge Your Feelings

I feel irritated about _____

_____

_____

_____

_____

_____

_____

_____

_____

Do the Heart Center Pose and say: *I accept all of these feelings.*
Or, *What if it's possible for me to accept all of these feelings?*

In my body, I notice _____

_____

_____

Move your body

Do the Energy Hookup.

Do the Heart Center Pose and say: *I accept all of this, and I'm open to new insights and to experiencing something else.*

Or, *What if it's possible for me to accept all of this, and to be open to new insights and to experiencing something else.*

Get Curious

I feel curious about _____

_____

_____

_____

In my body, I notice _____

_____

_____

Get Creative

Refuturing Statements:

♥ *What if it's possible* _____

♥ *What if it's possible* _____

♥ *What if it's possible* _____

♥ *What if it's possible* _____

♥ *What if it's possible* _____

Do the Heart Center Pose and say your Refuturing Statements aloud.

I choose _____

Say your Choose Statement several times aloud,
ideally while doing the Power Pose and looking into a mirror.

When I open to the Universe _____

_____

_____

_____

Get Courageous

What's next? _____

*My **one** next step is to* _____

_____

_____

I'll do it by _____

Do the Heart Center Pose and imagine yourself taking the action you just wrote about.

I feel _____

_____

In my body, I notice _____

_____

Write the action on your calendar. Do the Power Pose and *feel* yourself completing it.

Irritated

Acknowledge Your Feelings

I feel irritated about _____

_____

_____

_____

_____

_____

_____

_____

_____

_____

Do the Heart Center Pose and say: *I accept all of these feelings.*
Or, *What if it's possible for me to accept all of these feelings?*

In my body, I notice _____

_____

_____

Move your body

Do the Energy Hookup.

Do the Heart Center Pose and say: *I accept all of this, and I'm open to new insights
    and to experiencing something else.*

Or, *What if it's possible for me to accept all of this, and to be open to new insights
    and to experiencing something else.*

Get Curious

I feel curious about _____

_____

_____

_____

In my body, I notice _____

_____

_____

Get Creative

Refuturing Statements:

♥ *What if it's possible* _____

♥ *What if it's possible* _____

♥ *What if it's possible* _____

♥ *What if it's possible* _____

♥ *What if it's possible* _____

Do the Heart Center Pose and say your Refuturing Statements aloud.

I choose _____

**Say your Choose Statement several times aloud,
ideally while doing the Power Pose and looking into a mirror.**

When I open to the Universe _____

_____

_____

_____

Get Courageous

What's next? _____

*My **one** next step is to* _____

_____

_____

I'll do it by _____

Do the Heart Center Pose and imagine yourself taking the action you just wrote about.

I feel _____

_____

In my body, I notice _____

_____

Write the action on your calendar. Do the Power Pose and *feel* yourself completing it.

Overwhelmed

Acknowledge Your Feelings

I feel overwhelmed about _____
_____
_____
_____
_____
_____
_____
_____
_____
_____

Do the Heart Center Pose and say: *I accept all of these feelings.*
Or, *What if it's possible for me to accept all of these feelings?*

In my body, I notice _____
_____
_____

Move your body

Do the Energy Hookup.

Do the Heart Center Pose and say: *I accept all of this, and I'm open to new insights and to experiencing something else.*
Or, *What if it's possible for me to accept all of this, and to be open to new insights and to experiencing something else.*

Get Curious

I feel curious about _____
_____
_____

In my body, I notice _____
_____
_____

Get Creative

Refuturing Statements:

♥ *What if it's possible* _____

♥ *What if it's possible* _____

♥ *What if it's possible* _____

♥ *What if it's possible* _____

♥ *What if it's possible* _____

Do the Heart Center Pose and say your Refuturing Statements aloud.

I choose _____

**Say your Choose Statement several times aloud,
ideally while doing the Power Pose and looking into a mirror.**

When I open to the Universe _____

_____

_____

_____

Get Courageous

What's next? _____

*My **one** next step is to* _____

_____

_____

I'll do it by _____

Do the Heart Center Pose and imagine yourself taking the action you just wrote about.

I feel _____

_____

In my body, I notice _____

_____

Write the action on your calendar. Do the Power Pose and *feel* yourself completing it.

Overwhelmed

Acknowledge Your Feelings

I feel overwhelmed about _____

_____

_____

_____

_____

_____

_____

_____

_____

_____

Do the Heart Center Pose and say: *I accept all of these feelings.*
Or, *What if it's possible for me to accept all of these feelings?*

In my body, I notice _____

_____

_____

Move your body

Do the Energy Hookup.

Do the Heart Center Pose and say: *I accept all of this, and I'm open to new insights
     and to experiencing something else.*

Or, *What if it's possible for me to accept all of this, and to be open to new insights
     and to experiencing something else.*

Get Curious

I feel curious about _____

_____

_____

_____

In my body, I notice _____

_____

_____

Get Creative

Refuturing Statements:

♥ *What if it's possible* _____

♥ *What if it's possible* _____

♥ *What if it's possible* _____

♥ *What if it's possible* _____

♥ *What if it's possible* _____

Do the Heart Center Pose and say your Refuturing Statements aloud.

I choose _____

**Say your Choose Statement several times aloud,
ideally while doing the Power Pose and looking into a mirror.**

When I open to the Universe _____

_____

_____

_____

Get Courageous

What's next? _____

*My **one** next step is to* _____

_____

_____

I'll do it by _____

Do the Heart Center Pose and imagine yourself taking the action you just wrote about.

I feel _____

_____

In my body, I notice _____

_____

Write the action on your calendar. Do the Power Pose and *feel* yourself completing it.

Pressured

Acknowledge Your Feelings

I feel pressured about _____
_____
_____
_____
_____
_____
_____
_____
_____
_____

Do the Heart Center Pose and say: *I accept all of these feelings.*
Or, *What if it's possible for me to accept all of these feelings?*

In my body, I notice _____
_____
_____

Move your body

Do the Energy Hookup.

Do the Heart Center Pose and say: *I accept all of this, and I'm open to new insights and to experiencing something else.*

Or, *What if it's possible for me to accept all of this, and to be open to new insights and to experiencing something else.*

Get Curious

I feel curious about _____
_____
_____

In my body, I notice _____
_____
_____

Get Creative

Refuturing Statements:

♥ *What if it's possible* _____

♥ *What if it's possible* _____

♥ *What if it's possible* _____

♥ *What if it's possible* _____

♥ *What if it's possible* _____

Do the Heart Center Pose and say your Refuturing Statements aloud.

I choose _____

Say your Choose Statement several times aloud,
ideally while doing the Power Pose and looking into a mirror.

When I open to the Universe _____

_____

_____

_____

Get Courageous

What's next? _____

*My **one** next step is to* _____

_____

_____

I'll do it by _____

Do the Heart Center Pose and imagine yourself taking the action you just wrote about.

I feel _____

_____

In my body, I notice _____

_____

Write the action on your calendar. Do the Power Pose and *feel* yourself completing it.

Pressured

Acknowledge Your Feelings

I feel pressured about _____

_____

_____

_____

_____

_____

_____

_____

_____

Do the Heart Center Pose and say: *I accept all of these feelings.*
Or, *What if it's possible for me to accept all of these feelings?*

In my body, I notice _____

_____

_____

Move your body

Do the Energy Hookup.

Do the Heart Center Pose and say: *I accept all of this, and I'm open to new insights
      and to experiencing something else.*

Or, *What if it's possible for me to accept all of this, and to be open to new insights
      and to experiencing something else.*

Get Curious

I feel curious about _____

_____

_____

_____

In my body, I notice _____

_____

_____

Get Creative

Refuturing Statements:

♥ *What if it's possible* _____

♥ *What if it's possible* _____

♥ *What if it's possible* _____

♥ *What if it's possible* _____

♥ *What if it's possible* _____

Do the Heart Center Pose and say your Refuturing Statements aloud.

I choose _____

**Say your Choose Statement several times aloud,
ideally while doing the Power Pose and looking into a mirror.**

When I open to the Universe _____

_____

_____

_____

Get Courageous

What's next? _____

*My **one** next step is to* _____

_____

I'll do it by _____

Do the Heart Center Pose and imagine yourself taking the action you just wrote about.

I feel _____

_____

In my body, I notice _____

_____

Write the action on your calendar. Do the Power Pose and *feel* yourself completing it.

Shocked

Acknowledge Your Feelings

I feel shocked about _____

_____

_____

_____

_____

_____

_____

_____

_____

_____

Do the Heart Center Pose and say: *I accept all of these feelings.*
Or, *What if it's possible for me to accept all of these feelings?*

In my body, I notice _____

_____

_____

Move your body

Do the Energy Hookup.

Do the Heart Center Pose and say: *I accept all of this, and I'm open to new insights and to experiencing something else.*

Or, *What if it's possible for me to accept all of this, and to be open to new insights and to experiencing something else.*

Get Curious

I feel curious about _____

_____

_____

In my body, I notice _____

_____

_____

Get Creative

Refuturing Statements:

♥ *What if it's possible* _____

♥ *What if it's possible* _____

♥ *What if it's possible* _____

♥ *What if it's possible* _____

♥ *What if it's possible* _____

Do the Heart Center Pose and say your Refuturing Statements aloud.

I choose _____

Say your Choose Statement several times aloud,
ideally while doing the Power Pose and looking into a mirror.

When I open to the Universe _____

_____

_____

_____

Get Courageous

What's next? _____

*My **one** next step is to* _____

_____

I'll do it by _____

Do the Heart Center Pose and imagine yourself taking the action you just wrote about.

I feel _____

_____

In my body, I notice _____

_____

Write the action on your calendar. Do the Power Pose and *feel* yourself completing it.

Shocked

Acknowledge Your Feelings

I feel shocked about _____

_____

_____

_____

_____

_____

_____

_____

_____

Do the Heart Center Pose and say: *I accept all of these feelings.*
Or, *What if it's possible for me to accept all of these feelings?*

In my body, I notice _____

_____

_____

Move your body

Do the Energy Hookup.

Do the Heart Center Pose and say: *I accept all of this, and I'm open to new insights
    and to experiencing something else.*
Or, *What if it's possible for me to accept all of this, and to be open to new insights
    and to experiencing something else.*

Get Curious

I feel curious about _____

_____

_____

_____

In my body, I notice _____

_____

_____

Get Creative

Refuturing Statements:

♥ *What if it's possible* _____

♥ *What if it's possible* _____

♥ *What if it's possible* _____

♥ *What if it's possible* _____

♥ *What if it's possible* _____

Do the Heart Center Pose and say your Refuturing Statements aloud.

I choose _____

Say your Choose Statement several times aloud,
ideally while doing the Power Pose and looking into a mirror.

When I open to the Universe _____

_____

_____

_____

Get Courageous

What's next? _____

*My **one** next step is to* _____

_____

I'll do it by _____

Do the Heart Center Pose and imagine yourself taking the action you just wrote about.

I feel _____

_____

In my body, I notice _____

_____

Write the action on your calendar. Do the Power Pose and *feel* yourself completing it.

Humiliated

Acknowledge Your Feelings

I feel humiliated about _____

_____

_____

_____

_____

_____

_____

_____

_____

_____

Do the Heart Center Pose and say: *I accept all of these feelings.*
Or, *What if it's possible for me to accept all of these feelings?*

In my body, I notice _____

_____

_____

Move your body

Do the Energy Hookup.

Do the Heart Center Pose and say: *I accept all of this, and I'm open to new insights*
   and to experiencing something else.

Or, *What if it's possible for me to accept all of this, and to be open to new insights*
   and to experiencing something else.

Get Curious

I feel curious about _____

_____

_____

_____

In my body, I notice _____

_____

_____

Get Creative

Refuturing Statements:

♥ *What if it's possible* _____

♥ *What if it's possible* _____

♥ *What if it's possible* _____

♥ *What if it's possible* _____

♥ *What if it's possible* _____

Do the Heart Center Pose and say your Refuturing Statements aloud.

I choose _____

**Say your Choose Statement several times aloud,
ideally while doing the Power Pose and looking into a mirror.**

When I open to the Universe _____

_____

_____

_____

Get Courageous

What's next? _____

*My **one** next step is to* _____

_____

I'll do it by _____

Do the Heart Center Pose and imagine yourself taking the action you just wrote about.

I feel _____

_____

In my body, I notice _____

_____

Write the action on your calendar. Do the Power Pose and *feel* yourself completing it.

Humiliated

Acknowledge Your Feelings

I feel humiliated about _____

_____

_____

_____

_____

_____

_____

_____

_____

_____

Do the Heart Center Pose and say: *I accept all of these feelings.*
Or, *What if it's possible for me to accept all of these feelings?*

In my body, I notice _____

_____

_____

Move your body

Do the Energy Hookup.

Do the Heart Center Pose and say: *I accept all of this, and I'm open to new insights*
and to experiencing something else.

Or, *What if it's possible for me to accept all of this, and to be open to new insights*
and to experiencing something else.

Get Curious

I feel curious about _____

_____

_____

In my body, I notice _____

_____

_____

Get Creative

Refuturing Statements:

♥ *What if it's possible* _____

♥ *What if it's possible* _____

♥ *What if it's possible* _____

♥ *What if it's possible* _____

♥ *What if it's possible* _____

Do the Heart Center Pose and say your Refuturing Statements aloud.

I choose _____

**Say your Choose Statement several times aloud,
ideally while doing the Power Pose and looking into a mirror.**

When I open to the Universe _____

_____

_____

_____

Get Courageous

What's next? _____

*My **one** next step is to* _____

_____

I'll do it by _____

Do the Heart Center Pose and imagine yourself taking the action you just wrote about.

I feel _____

_____

In my body, I notice _____

_____

Write the action on your calendar. Do the Power Pose and *feel* yourself completing it.

Disgusted

Acknowledge Your Feelings

I feel disgusted about _____

_____

_____

_____

_____

_____

_____

_____

Do the Heart Center Pose and say: *I accept all of these feelings.*
Or, *What if it's possible for me to accept all of these feelings?*

In my body, I notice _____

_____

_____

Move your body

Do the Energy Hookup.

Do the Heart Center Pose and say: *I accept all of this, and I'm open to new insights*
and to experiencing something else.

Or, *What if it's possible for me to accept all of this, and to be open to new insights*
and to experiencing something else.

Get Curious

I feel curious about _____

_____

_____

_____

In my body, I notice _____

_____

_____

_____

Get Creative

Refuturing Statements:

♥ *What if it's possible* _____

♥ *What if it's possible* _____

♥ *What if it's possible* _____

♥ *What if it's possible* _____

♥ *What if it's possible* _____

Do the Heart Center Pose and say your Refuturing Statements aloud.

I choose _____

**Say your Choose Statement several times aloud,
ideally while doing the Power Pose and looking into a mirror.**

When I open to the Universe _____

_____

_____

_____

Get Courageous

What's next? _____

*My **one** next step is to* _____

_____

_____

I'll do it by _____

Do the Heart Center Pose and imagine yourself taking the action you just wrote about.

I feel _____

_____

In my body, I notice _____

_____

Write the action on your calendar. Do the Power Pose and *feel* yourself completing it.

Disgusted

Acknowledge Your Feelings

I feel disgusted about _____

_____

_____

_____

_____

_____

_____

_____

Do the Heart Center Pose and say: *I accept all of these feelings.*
Or, *What if it's possible for me to accept all of these feelings?*

In my body, I notice _____

_____

_____

Move your body

Do the Energy Hookup.

Do the Heart Center Pose and say: *I accept all of this, and I'm open to new insights
and to experiencing something else.*

Or, *What if it's possible for me to accept all of this, and to be open to new insights
and to experiencing something else.*

Get Curious

I feel curious about _____

_____

_____

In my body, I notice _____

_____

_____

Get Creative

Refuturing Statements:

♥ *What if it's possible* _____

♥ *What if it's possible* _____

♥ *What if it's possible* _____

♥ *What if it's possible* _____

♥ *What if it's possible* _____

Do the Heart Center Pose and say your Refuturing Statements aloud.

I choose _____

Say your Choose Statement several times aloud,
ideally while doing the Power Pose and looking into a mirror.

When I open to the Universe _____

_____

_____

_____

Get Courageous

What's next? _____

*My **one** next step is to* _____

_____

I'll do it by _____

Do the Heart Center Pose and imagine yourself taking the action you just wrote about.

I feel _____

_____

In my body, I notice _____

_____

Write the action on your calendar. Do the Power Pose and *feel* yourself completing it.

Excited

Acknowledge Your Feelings

I feel excited about _____

_____

_____

_____

_____

_____

_____

_____

_____

Do the Heart Center Pose and say: *I accept all of these feelings.*
Or, *What if it's possible for me to accept all of these feelings?*

In my body, I notice _____

_____

_____

Move your body

Do the Energy Hookup.

Do the Heart Center Pose and say: *I accept all of this, and I'm open to new insights and to experiencing something else.*

Or, *What if it's possible for me to accept all of this, and to be open to new insights and to experiencing something else.*

Get Curious

I feel curious about _____

_____

_____

In my body, I notice _____

_____

_____

Get Creative

Refuturing Statements:

♥ *What if it's possible* _____

♥ *What if it's possible* _____

♥ *What if it's possible* _____

♥ *What if it's possible* _____

♥ *What if it's possible* _____

Do the Heart Center Pose and say your Refuturing Statements aloud.

I choose _____

**Say your Choose Statement several times aloud,
ideally while doing the Power Pose and looking into a mirror.**

When I open to the Universe _____

_____

_____

_____

Get Courageous

What's next? _____

*My **one** next step is to* _____

_____

_____

I'll do it by _____

Do the Heart Center Pose and imagine yourself taking the action you just wrote about.

I feel _____

_____

In my body, I notice _____

_____

Write the action on your calendar. Do the Power Pose and *feel* yourself completing it.

Excited

Acknowledge Your Feelings

I feel excited about _____
_____
_____
_____
_____
_____
_____
_____
_____

Do the Heart Center Pose and say: *I accept all of these feelings.*
Or, *What if it's possible for me to accept all of these feelings?*

In my body, I notice _____
_____
_____

Move your body

Do the Energy Hookup.

Do the Heart Center Pose and say: *I accept all of this, and I'm open to new insights*
　　and to experiencing something else.
Or, *What if it's possible for me to accept all of this, and to be open to new insights*
　　and to experiencing something else.

Get Curious

I feel curious about _____
_____
_____
_____

In my body, I notice _____
_____
_____

Get Creative

Refuturing Statements:

♥ *What if it's possible* _____

♥ *What if it's possible* _____

♥ *What if it's possible* _____

♥ *What if it's possible* _____

♥ *What if it's possible* _____

Do the Heart Center Pose and say your Refuturing Statements aloud.

I choose _____

**Say your Choose Statement several times aloud,
ideally while doing the Power Pose and looking into a mirror.**

When I open to the Universe _____

_____

_____

_____

Get Courageous

What's next? _____

*My **one** next step is to* _____

_____

_____

I'll do it by _____

Do the Heart Center Pose and imagine yourself taking the action you just wrote about.

I feel _____

_____

In my body, I notice _____

_____

Write the action on your calendar. Do the Power Pose and *feel* yourself completing it.

Hopeful

Acknowledge Your Feelings

I feel hopeful about _____

_____

_____

_____

_____

_____

_____

_____

_____

Do the Heart Center Pose and say: *I accept all of these feelings.*
Or, *What if it's possible for me to accept all of these feelings?*

In my body, I notice _____

_____

_____

Move your body

Do the Energy Hookup.

Do the Heart Center Pose and say: *I accept all of this, and I'm open to new insights and to experiencing something else.*

Or, *What if it's possible for me to accept all of this, and to be open to new insights and to experiencing something else.*

Get Curious

I feel curious about _____

_____

_____

_____

In my body, I notice _____

_____

_____

Get Creative

Refuturing Statements:

♥ *What if it's possible* _____

♥ *What if it's possible* _____

♥ *What if it's possible* _____

♥ *What if it's possible* _____

♥ *What if it's possible* _____

Do the Heart Center Pose and say your Refuturing Statements aloud.

I choose _____

**Say your Choose Statement several times aloud,
ideally while doing the Power Pose and looking into a mirror.**

When I open to the Universe _____

_____

_____

_____

Get Courageous

What's next? _____

*My **one** next step is to* _____

_____

I'll do it by _____

Do the Heart Center Pose and imagine yourself taking the action you just wrote about.

I feel _____

_____

In my body, I notice _____

_____

Write the action on your calendar. Do the Power Pose and *feel* yourself completing it.

Hopeful

Acknowledge Your Feelings

I feel hopeful about _____

_____

_____

_____

_____

_____

_____

_____

_____

Do the Heart Center Pose and say: *I accept all of these feelings.*
Or, *What if it's possible for me to accept all of these feelings?*

In my body, I notice _____

_____

_____

Move your body

Do the Energy Hookup.

Do the Heart Center Pose and say: *I accept all of this, and I'm open to new insights and to experiencing something else.*

Or, *What if it's possible for me to accept all of this, and to be open to new insights and to experiencing something else.*

Get Curious

I feel curious about _____

_____

_____

_____

In my body, I notice _____

_____

_____

Get Creative

Refuturing Statements:

♥ *What if it's possible* _____

♥ *What if it's possible* _____

♥ *What if it's possible* _____

♥ *What if it's possible* _____

♥ *What if it's possible* _____

Do the Heart Center Pose and say your Refuturing Statements aloud.

I choose _____

Say your Choose Statement several times aloud,
ideally while doing the Power Pose and looking into a mirror.

When I open to the Universe _____

_____

_____

_____

Get Courageous

What's next? _____

*My **one** next step is to* _____

_____

I'll do it by _____

Do the Heart Center Pose and imagine yourself taking the action you just wrote about.

I feel _____

In my body, I notice _____

Write the action on your calendar. Do the Power Pose and *feel* yourself completing it.

Thrilled

Acknowledge Your Feelings

I feel thrilled about _____

_____

_____

_____

_____

_____

_____

_____

_____

_____

Do the Heart Center Pose and say: *I accept all of these feelings.*
Or, *What if it's possible for me to accept all of these feelings?*

In my body, I notice _____

_____

_____

Move your body

Do the Energy Hookup.

Do the Heart Center Pose and say: *I accept all of this, and I'm open to new insights
and to experiencing something else.*

Or, *What if it's possible for me to accept all of this, and to be open to new insights
and to experiencing something else.*

Get Curious

I feel curious about _____

_____

_____

_____

In my body, I notice _____

_____

_____

Get Creative

Refuturing Statements:

♥ *What if it's possible* _____

♥ *What if it's possible* _____

♥ *What if it's possible* _____

♥ *What if it's possible* _____

♥ *What if it's possible* _____

Do the Heart Center Pose and say your Refuturing Statements aloud.

I choose _____

Say your Choose Statement several times aloud,
ideally while doing the Power Pose and looking into a mirror.

When I open to the Universe _____

_____

_____

_____

Get Courageous

What's next? _____

*My **one** next step is to* _____

_____

I'll do it by _____

Do the Heart Center Pose and imagine yourself taking the action you just wrote about.

I feel _____

_____

In my body, I notice _____

_____

Write the action on your calendar. Do the Power Pose and *feel* yourself completing it.

Thrilled

Acknowledge Your Feelings

I feel thrilled about _____

_____

_____

_____

_____

_____

_____

_____

_____

Do the Heart Center Pose and say: *I accept all of these feelings.*
Or, *What if it's possible for me to accept all of these feelings?*

In my body, I notice _____

_____

_____

Move your body

Do the Energy Hookup.

Do the Heart Center Pose and say: *I accept all of this, and I'm open to new insights
     and to experiencing something else.*

Or, *What if it's possible for me to accept all of this, and to be open to new insights
     and to experiencing something else.*

Get Curious

I feel curious about _____

_____

_____

In my body, I notice _____

_____

_____

Get Creative

Refuturing Statements:

♥ *What if it's possible* _____

♥ *What if it's possible* _____

♥ *What if it's possible* _____

♥ *What if it's possible* _____

♥ *What if it's possible* _____

Do the Heart Center Pose and say your Refuturing Statements aloud.

I choose _____

Say your Choose Statement several times aloud,
ideally while doing the Power Pose and looking into a mirror.

When I open to the Universe _____

_____

_____

_____

Get Courageous

What's next? _____

*My **one** next step is to* _____

_____

_____

I'll do it by _____

Do the Heart Center Pose and imagine yourself taking the action you just wrote about.

I feel _____

_____

In my body, I notice _____

_____

Write the action on your calendar. Do the Power Pose and *feel* yourself completing it.

Delighted

Acknowledge Your Feelings

I feel delighted about _____

_____

_____

_____

_____

_____

_____

_____

_____

Do the Heart Center Pose and say: *I accept all of these feelings.*
Or, *What if it's possible for me to accept all of these feelings?*

In my body, I notice _____

_____

_____

Move your body

Do the Energy Hookup.

Do the Heart Center Pose and say: *I accept all of this, and I'm open to new insights and to experiencing something else.*

Or, *What if it's possible for me to accept all of this, and to be open to new insights and to experiencing something else.*

Get Curious

I feel curious about _____

_____

_____

_____

In my body, I notice _____

_____

_____

Get Creative

Refuturing Statements:

♥ *What if it's possible* _____

♥ *What if it's possible* _____

♥ *What if it's possible* _____

♥ *What if it's possible* _____

♥ *What if it's possible* _____

Do the Heart Center Pose and say your Refuturing Statements aloud.

I choose _____

Say your Choose Statement several times aloud,
ideally while doing the Power Pose and looking into a mirror.

When I open to the Universe _____

_____

_____

_____

Get Courageous

What's next? _____

*My **one** next step is to* _____

_____

_____

I'll do it by _____

Do the Heart Center Pose and imagine yourself taking the action you just wrote about.

I feel _____

_____

In my body, I notice _____

_____

Write the action on your calendar. Do the Power Pose and *feel* yourself completing it.

144

Delighted

Acknowledge Your Feelings

I feel delighted about _____

_____

_____

_____

_____

_____

_____

_____

_____

_____

Do the Heart Center Pose and say: *I accept all of these feelings.*
Or, *What if it's possible for me to accept all of these feelings?*

In my body, I notice _____

_____

_____

Move your body

Do the Energy Hookup.

Do the Heart Center Pose and say: *I accept all of this, and I'm open to new insights and to experiencing something else.*

Or, *What if it's possible for me to accept all of this, and to be open to new insights and to experiencing something else.*

Get Curious

I feel curious about _____

_____

_____

_____

In my body, I notice _____

_____

_____

Get Creative

Refuturing Statements:

♥ *What if it's possible* _____

♥ *What if it's possible* _____

♥ *What if it's possible* _____

♥ *What if it's possible* _____

♥ *What if it's possible* _____

Do the Heart Center Pose and say your Refuturing Statements aloud.

I choose _____

**Say your Choose Statement several times aloud,
ideally while doing the Power Pose and looking into a mirror.**

When I open to the Universe _____

_____

_____

_____

Get Courageous

What's next? _____

*My **one** next step is to* _____

_____

_____

I'll do it by _____

Do the Heart Center Pose and imagine yourself taking the action you just wrote about.

I feel _____

_____

In my body, I notice _____

_____

Write the action on your calendar. Do the Power Pose and *feel* yourself completing it.

Happy

Acknowledge Your Feelings

I feel happy about _____

_____

_____

_____

_____

_____

_____

_____

_____

_____

Do the Heart Center Pose and say: *I accept all of these feelings.*
Or, *What if it's possible for me to accept all of these feelings?*

In my body, I notice _____

_____

_____

Move your body

Do the Energy Hookup.

Do the Heart Center Pose and say: *I accept all of this, and I'm open to new insights
    and to experiencing something else.*

Or, *What if it's possible for me to accept all of this, and to be open to new insights
    and to experiencing something else.*

Get Curious

I feel curious about _____

_____

_____

_____

In my body, I notice _____

_____

_____

Get Creative

Refuturing Statements:

♥ *What if it's possible* _____

♥ *What if it's possible* _____

♥ *What if it's possible* _____

♥ *What if it's possible* _____

♥ *What if it's possible* _____

Do the Heart Center Pose and say your Refuturing Statements aloud.

I choose _____

Say your Choose Statement several times aloud,
ideally while doing the Power Pose and looking into a mirror.

When I open to the Universe _____

_____

_____

_____

Get Courageous

What's next? _____

*My **one** next step is to* _____

_____

_____

I'll do it by _____

Do the Heart Center Pose and imagine yourself taking the action you just wrote about.

I feel _____

_____

In my body, I notice _____

_____

Write the action on your calendar. Do the Power Pose and *feel* yourself completing it.

Happy

Acknowledge Your Feelings

I feel happy about _____

_____

_____

_____

_____

_____

_____

_____

_____

_____

Do the Heart Center Pose and say: *I accept all of these feelings.*
Or, *What if it's possible for me to accept all of these feelings?*

In my body, I notice _____

_____

_____

Move your body

Do the Energy Hookup.

Do the Heart Center Pose and say: *I accept all of this, and I'm open to new insights
and to experiencing something else.*

Or, *What if it's possible for me to accept all of this, and to be open to new insights
and to experiencing something else.*

Get Curious

I feel curious about _____

_____

_____

_____

In my body, I notice _____

_____

_____

Get Creative

Refuturing Statements:

♥ *What if it's possible* _____

♥ *What if it's possible* _____

♥ *What if it's possible* _____

♥ *What if it's possible* _____

♥ *What if it's possible* _____

Do the Heart Center Pose and say your Refuturing Statements aloud.

I choose _____

**Say your Choose Statement several times aloud,
ideally while doing the Power Pose and looking into a mirror.**

When I open to the Universe _____

_____

_____

_____

Get Courageous

What's next? _____

*My **one** next step is to* _____

_____

_____

I'll do it by _____

Do the Heart Center Pose and imagine yourself taking the action you just wrote about.

I feel _____

_____

In my body, I notice _____

_____

Write the action on your calendar. Do the Power Pose and *feel* yourself completing it.

Joyful

Acknowledge Your Feelings

I feel joyful about _____

_____

_____

_____

_____

_____

_____

_____

_____

_____

Do the Heart Center Pose and say: *I accept all of these feelings.*
Or, *What if it's possible for me to accept all of these feelings?*

In my body, I notice _____

_____

_____

Move your body

Do the Energy Hookup.

Do the Heart Center Pose and say: *I accept all of this, and I'm open to new insights and to experiencing something else.*

Or, *What if it's possible for me to accept all of this, and to be open to new insights and to experiencing something else.*

Get Curious

I feel curious about _____

_____

_____

_____

In my body, I notice _____

_____

_____

Get Creative

Refuturing Statements:

♥ *What if it's possible* _____

♥ *What if it's possible* _____

♥ *What if it's possible* _____

♥ *What if it's possible* _____

♥ *What if it's possible* _____

Do the Heart Center Pose and say your Refuturing Statements aloud.

I choose _____

Say your Choose Statement several times aloud,
ideally while doing the Power Pose and looking into a mirror.

When I open to the Universe _____

_____

_____

_____

Get Courageous

What's next? _____

*My **one** next step is to* _____

_____

_____

I'll do it by _____

Do the Heart Center Pose and imagine yourself taking the action you just wrote about.

I feel _____

_____

In my body, I notice _____

_____

Write the action on your calendar. Do the Power Pose and *feel* yourself completing it.

Joyful

Acknowledge Your Feelings

I feel joyful about _____

_____

_____

_____

_____

_____

_____

_____

_____

Do the Heart Center Pose and say: *I accept all of these feelings.*
Or, *What if it's possible for me to accept all of these feelings?*

In my body, I notice _____

_____

_____

Move your body

Do the Energy Hookup.

Do the Heart Center Pose and say: *I accept all of this, and I'm open to new insights and to experiencing something else.*

Or, *What if it's possible for me to accept all of this, and to be open to new insights and to experiencing something else.*

Get Curious

I feel curious about _____

_____

_____

_____

In my body, I notice _____

_____

_____

Get Creative

Refuturing Statements:

♥ *What if it's possible* _____

♥ *What if it's possible* _____

♥ *What if it's possible* _____

♥ *What if it's possible* _____

♥ *What if it's possible* _____

Do the Heart Center Pose and say your Refuturing Statements aloud.

I choose _____

**Say your Choose Statement several times aloud,
ideally while doing the Power Pose and looking into a mirror.**

When I open to the Universe _____

_____

_____

_____

Get Courageous

What's next? _____

*My **one** next step is to* _____

_____

_____

I'll do it by _____

Do the Heart Center Pose and imagine yourself taking the action you just wrote about.

I feel _____

_____

In my body, I notice _____

_____

Write the action on your calendar. Do the Power Pose and *feel* yourself completing it.

Surprised

Acknowledge Your Feelings

I feel surprised about _____

_____

_____

_____

_____

_____

_____

_____

_____

Do the Heart Center Pose and say: *I accept all of these feelings.*
Or, *What if it's possible for me to accept all of these feelings?*

In my body, I notice _____

_____

_____

Move your body

Do the Energy Hookup.

Do the Heart Center Pose and say: *I accept all of this, and I'm open to new insights
and to experiencing something else.*

Or, *What if it's possible for me to accept all of this, and to be open to new insights
and to experiencing something else.*

Get Curious

I feel curious about _____

_____

_____

_____

In my body, I notice _____

_____

_____

Get Creative

Refuturing Statements:

♥ *What if it's possible* _____

♥ *What if it's possible* _____

♥ *What if it's possible* _____

♥ *What if it's possible* _____

♥ *What if it's possible* _____

Do the Heart Center Pose and say your Refuturing Statements aloud.

I choose _____

**Say your Choose Statement several times aloud,
ideally while doing the Power Pose and looking into a mirror.**

When I open to the Universe _____

_____

_____

_____

Get Courageous

What's next? _____

My **one** *next step is to* _____

_____

I'll do it by _____

Do the Heart Center Pose and imagine yourself taking the action you just wrote about.

I feel _____

_____

In my body, I notice _____

_____

Write the action on your calendar. Do the Power Pose and *feel* yourself completing it.

Surprised

Acknowledge Your Feelings

I feel surprised about _____

_____

_____

_____

_____

_____

_____

_____

_____

Do the Heart Center Pose and say: *I accept all of these feelings.*
Or, *What if it's possible for me to accept all of these feelings?*

In my body, I notice _____

_____

_____

Move your body

Do the Energy Hookup.

Do the Heart Center Pose and say: *I accept all of this, and I'm open to new insights
and to experiencing something else.*

Or, *What if it's possible for me to accept all of this, and to be open to new insights
and to experiencing something else.*

Get Curious

I feel curious about _____

_____

_____

_____

In my body, I notice _____

_____

_____

Get Creative

Refuturing Statements:

♥ *What if it's possible* _____

♥ *What if it's possible* _____

♥ *What if it's possible* _____

♥ *What if it's possible* _____

♥ *What if it's possible* _____

Do the Heart Center Pose and say your Refuturing Statements aloud.

I choose _____

Say your Choose Statement several times aloud,
ideally while doing the Power Pose and looking into a mirror.

When I open to the Universe _____

_____

_____

_____

Get Courageous

What's next? _____

My **one** *next step is to* _____

_____

_____

I'll do it by _____

Do the Heart Center Pose and imagine yourself taking the action you just wrote about.

I feel _____

_____

In my body, I notice _____

_____

Write the action on your calendar. Do the Power Pose and *feel* yourself completing it.

Enchanted

Acknowledge Your Feelings

I feel enchanted about _____

_____

_____

_____

_____

_____

_____

_____

_____

Do the Heart Center Pose and say: *I accept all of these feelings.*
Or, *What if it's possible for me to accept all of these feelings?*

In my body, I notice _____

_____

_____

Move your body

Do the Energy Hookup.

Do the Heart Center Pose and say: *I accept all of this, and I'm open to new insights
and to experiencing something else.*

Or, *What if it's possible for me to accept all of this, and to be open to new insights
and to experiencing something else.*

Get Curious

I feel curious about _____

_____

_____

_____

In my body, I notice _____

_____

_____

Get Creative

Refuturing Statements:

♥ *What if it's possible* _____

♥ *What if it's possible* _____

♥ *What if it's possible* _____

♥ *What if it's possible* _____

♥ *What if it's possible* _____

Do the Heart Center Pose and say your Refuturing Statements aloud.

I choose _____

Say your Choose Statement several times aloud,
ideally while doing the Power Pose and looking into a mirror.

When I open to the Universe _____

_____

_____

_____

Get Courageous

What's next? _____

*My **one** next step is to* _____

_____

I'll do it by _____

Do the Heart Center Pose and imagine yourself taking the action you just wrote about.

I feel _____

_____

In my body, I notice _____

_____

Write the action on your calendar. Do the Power Pose and *feel* yourself completing it.

Enchanted

Acknowledge Your Feelings

I feel enchanted about _____

_____

_____

_____

_____

_____

_____

_____

_____

Do the Heart Center Pose and say: *I accept all of these feelings.*
Or, *What if it's possible for me to accept all of these feelings?*

In my body, I notice _____

_____

_____

Move your body

Do the Energy Hookup.

Do the Heart Center Pose and say: *I accept all of this, and I'm open to new insights and to experiencing something else.*

Or, *What if it's possible for me to accept all of this, and to be open to new insights and to experiencing something else.*

Get Curious

I feel curious about _____

_____

_____

In my body, I notice _____

_____

_____

Get Creative

Refuturing Statements:

♥ *What if it's possible* _____

♥ *What if it's possible* _____

♥ *What if it's possible* _____

♥ *What if it's possible* _____

♥ *What if it's possible* _____

Do the Heart Center Pose and say your Refuturing Statements aloud.

I choose _____

Say your Choose Statement several times aloud,
ideally while doing the Power Pose and looking into a mirror.

When I open to the Universe _____

_____

_____

_____

Get Courageous

What's next? _____

My **one** *next step is to* _____

_____

_____

I'll do it by _____

Do the Heart Center Pose and imagine yourself taking the action you just wrote about.

I feel _____

_____

In my body, I notice _____

_____

Write the action on your calendar. Do the Power Pose and *feel* yourself completing it.

Loving

Acknowledge Your Feelings

I feel loving about _____

_____

_____

_____

_____

_____

_____

_____

Do the Heart Center Pose and say: *I accept all of these feelings.*
Or, *What if it's possible for me to accept all of these feelings?*

In my body, I notice _____

_____

_____

Move your body

Do the Energy Hookup.

Do the Heart Center Pose and say: *I accept all of this, and I'm open to new insights and to experiencing something else.*

Or, *What if it's possible for me to accept all of this, and to be open to new insights and to experiencing something else.*

Get Curious

I feel curious about _____

_____

_____

In my body, I notice _____

_____

_____

Get Creative

Refuturing Statements:

♥ *What if it's possible* _____

♥ *What if it's possible* _____

♥ *What if it's possible* _____

♥ *What if it's possible* _____

♥ *What if it's possible* _____

Do the Heart Center Pose and say your Refuturing Statements aloud.

I choose _____

**Say your Choose Statement several times aloud,
ideally while doing the Power Pose and looking into a mirror.**

When I open to the Universe _____

_____

_____

_____

Get Courageous

What's next? _____

*My **one** next step is to* _____

_____

I'll do it by _____

Do the Heart Center Pose and imagine yourself taking the action you just wrote about.

I feel _____

_____

In my body, I notice _____

_____

Write the action on your calendar. Do the Power Pose and *feel* yourself completing it.

Loving

Acknowledge Your Feelings

I feel loving about _____

_____

_____

_____

_____

_____

_____

_____

_____

_____

Do the Heart Center Pose and say: *I accept all of these feelings.*
Or, *What if it's possible for me to accept all of these feelings?*

In my body, I notice _____

_____

_____

Move your body

Do the Energy Hookup.

Do the Heart Center Pose and say: *I accept all of this, and I'm open to new insights*
   and to experiencing something else.

Or, *What if it's possible for me to accept all of this, and to be open to new insights*
   and to experiencing something else.

Get Curious

I feel curious about _____

_____

_____

_____

In my body, I notice _____

_____

_____

Get Creative

Refuturing Statements:

♥ *What if it's possible* _____

♥ *What if it's possible* _____

♥ *What if it's possible* _____

♥ *What if it's possible* _____

♥ *What if it's possible* _____

Do the Heart Center Pose and say your Refuturing Statements aloud.

I choose _____

Say your Choose Statement several times aloud,
ideally while doing the Power Pose and looking into a mirror.

When I open to the Universe _____

_____

_____

_____

Get Courageous

What's next? _____

*My **one** next step is to* _____

_____

I'll do it by _____

Do the Heart Center Pose and imagine yourself taking the action you just wrote about.

I feel _____

_____

In my body, I notice _____

_____

Write the action on your calendar. Do the Power Pose and *feel* yourself completing it.

Vulnerable

Acknowledge Your Feelings

I feel vulnerable about _____

_____

_____

_____

_____

_____

_____

_____

_____

Do the Heart Center Pose and say: *I accept all of these feelings.*
Or, *What if it's possible for me to accept all of these feelings?*

In my body, I notice _____

_____

_____

Move your body

Do the Energy Hookup.

Do the Heart Center Pose and say: *I accept all of this, and I'm open to new insights and to experiencing something else.*

Or, *What if it's possible for me to accept all of this, and to be open to new insights and to experiencing something else.*

Get Curious

I feel curious about _____

_____

_____

In my body, I notice _____

_____

_____

Get Creative

Refuturing Statements:

♥ *What if it's possible* _____

♥ *What if it's possible* _____

♥ *What if it's possible* _____

♥ *What if it's possible* _____

♥ *What if it's possible* _____

Do the Heart Center Pose and say your Refuturing Statements aloud.

I choose _____

Say your Choose Statement several times aloud,
ideally while doing the Power Pose and looking into a mirror.

When I open to the Universe _____

_____

_____

_____

Get Courageous

What's next? _____

*My **one** next step is to* _____

_____

I'll do it by _____

Do the Heart Center Pose and imagine yourself taking the action you just wrote about.

I feel _____

_____

In my body, I notice _____

_____

Write the action on your calendar. Do the Power Pose and *feel* yourself completing it.

168

Vulnerable

Acknowledge Your Feelings

I feel vulnerable about _____

_____

_____

_____

_____

_____

_____

_____

_____

Do the Heart Center Pose and say: *I accept all of these feelings.*
Or, *What if it's possible for me to accept all of these feelings?*

In my body, I notice _____

_____

_____

Move your body

Do the Energy Hookup.

Do the Heart Center Pose and say: *I accept all of this, and I'm open to new insights and to experiencing something else.*

Or, *What if it's possible for me to accept all of this, and to be open to new insights and to experiencing something else.*

Get Curious

I feel curious about _____

_____

_____

_____

In my body, I notice _____

_____

_____

Get Creative

Refuturing Statements:

♥ *What if it's possible* _____

♥ *What if it's possible* _____

♥ *What if it's possible* _____

♥ *What if it's possible* _____

♥ *What if it's possible* _____

Do the Heart Center Pose and say your Refuturing Statements aloud.

I choose _____

**Say your Choose Statement several times aloud,
ideally while doing the Power Pose and looking into a mirror.**

When I open to the Universe _____

_____

_____

_____

Get Courageous

What's next? _____

*My **one** next step is to* _____

_____

_____

I'll do it by _____

Do the Heart Center Pose and imagine yourself taking the action you just wrote about.

I feel _____

_____

In my body, I notice _____

_____

Write the action on your calendar. Do the Power Pose and *feel* yourself completing it.

Calm

Acknowledge Your Feelings

I feel calm about _____

_____

_____

_____

_____

_____

_____

_____

_____

_____

Do the Heart Center Pose and say: *I accept all of these feelings.*
Or, *What if it's possible for me to accept all of these feelings?*

In my body, I notice _____

_____

_____

Move your body

Do the Energy Hookup.

Do the Heart Center Pose and say: *I accept all of this, and I'm open to new insights and to experiencing something else.*

Or, *What if it's possible for me to accept all of this, and to be open to new insights and to experiencing something else.*

Get Curious

I feel curious about _____

_____

_____

_____

In my body, I notice _____

_____

_____

Get Creative

Refuturing Statements:

♥ *What if it's possible* _____

♥ *What if it's possible* _____

♥ *What if it's possible* _____

♥ *What if it's possible* _____

♥ *What if it's possible* _____

Do the Heart Center Pose and say your Refuturing Statements aloud.

I choose _____

**Say your Choose Statement several times aloud,
ideally while doing the Power Pose and looking into a mirror.**

When I open to the Universe _____

_____

_____

_____

Get Courageous

What's next? _____

*My **one** next step is to* _____

_____

I'll do it by _____

Do the Heart Center Pose and imagine yourself taking the action you just wrote about.

I feel _____

_____

In my body, I notice _____

_____

Write the action on your calendar. Do the Power Pose and *feel* yourself completing it.

Calm

Acknowledge Your Feelings

I feel calm about _____

_____

_____

_____

_____

_____

_____

_____

_____

_____

Do the Heart Center Pose and say: *I accept all of these feelings.*
Or, *What if it's possible for me to accept all of these feelings?*

In my body, I notice _____

_____

_____

Move your body

Do the Energy Hookup.

Do the Heart Center Pose and say: *I accept all of this, and I'm open to new insights
and to experiencing something else.*

Or, *What if it's possible for me to accept all of this, and to be open to new insights
and to experiencing something else.*

Get Curious

I feel curious about _____

_____

_____

_____

In my body, I notice _____

_____

_____

Get Creative

Refuturing Statements:

♥ *What if it's possible* _____

♥ *What if it's possible* _____

♥ *What if it's possible* _____

♥ *What if it's possible* _____

♥ *What if it's possible* _____

Do the Heart Center Pose and say your Refuturing Statements aloud.

I choose _____

Say your Choose Statement several times aloud,
ideally while doing the Power Pose and looking into a mirror.

When I open to the Universe _____

_____

_____

_____

Get Courageous

What's next? _____

*My **one** next step is to* _____

_____

_____

I'll do it by _____

Do the Heart Center Pose and imagine yourself taking the action you just wrote about.

I feel _____

_____

In my body, I notice _____

_____

Write the action on your calendar. Do the Power Pose and *feel* yourself completing it.

Peaceful

Acknowledge Your Feelings

I feel peaceful about _____

_____

_____

_____

_____

_____

_____

_____

_____

Do the Heart Center Pose and say: *I accept all of these feelings.*
Or, *What if it's possible for me to accept all of these feelings?*

In my body, I notice _____

_____

_____

Move your body

Do the Energy Hookup.

Do the Heart Center Pose and say: *I accept all of this, and I'm open to new insights
and to experiencing something else.*

Or, *What if it's possible for me to accept all of this, and to be open to new insights
and to experiencing something else.*

Get Curious

I feel curious about _____

_____

_____

In my body, I notice _____

_____

_____

Get Creative

Refuturing Statements:

♥ *What if it's possible* _____

♥ *What if it's possible* _____

♥ *What if it's possible* _____

♥ *What if it's possible* _____

♥ *What if it's possible* _____

Do the Heart Center Pose and say your Refuturing Statements aloud.

I choose _____

Say your Choose Statement several times aloud,
ideally while doing the Power Pose and looking into a mirror.

When I open to the Universe _____

_____

_____

_____

Get Courageous

What's next? _____

*My **one** next step is to* _____

_____

I'll do it by _____

Do the Heart Center Pose and imagine yourself taking the action you just wrote about.

I feel _____

_____

In my body, I notice _____

_____

Write the action on your calendar. Do the Power Pose and *feel* yourself completing it.

Peaceful

Acknowledge Your Feelings

I feel peaceful about _____
_____
_____
_____
_____
_____
_____
_____
_____

Do the Heart Center Pose and say: *I accept all of these feelings.*
Or, *What if it's possible for me to accept all of these feelings?*

In my body, I notice _____
_____
_____

Move your body

Do the Energy Hookup.

Do the Heart Center Pose and say: *I accept all of this, and I'm open to new insights
     and to experiencing something else.*

Or, *What if it's possible for me to accept all of this, and to be open to new insights
     and to experiencing something else.*

Get Curious

I feel curious about _____
_____
_____
_____

In my body, I notice _____
_____
_____

Get Creative

Refuturing Statements:

♥ *What if it's possible* _____

♥ *What if it's possible* _____

♥ *What if it's possible* _____

♥ *What if it's possible* _____

♥ *What if it's possible* _____

Do the Heart Center Pose and say your Refuturing Statements aloud.

I choose _____

Say your Choose Statement several times aloud,
ideally while doing the Power Pose and looking into a mirror.

When I open to the Universe _____

_____

_____

_____

Get Courageous

What's next? _____

*My **one** next step is to* _____

_____

_____

I'll do it by _____

Do the Heart Center Pose and imagine yourself taking the action you just wrote about.

I feel _____

_____

In my body, I notice _____

_____

Write the action on your calendar. Do the Power Pose and *feel* yourself completing it.

Tranquil

Acknowledge Your Feelings

I feel tranquil about _____

_____

_____

_____

_____

_____

_____

_____

_____

Do the Heart Center Pose and say: *I accept all of these feelings.*
Or, *What if it's possible for me to accept all of these feelings?*

In my body, I notice _____

_____

_____

Move your body

Do the Energy Hookup.

Do the Heart Center Pose and say: *I accept all of this, and I'm open to new insights
and to experiencing something else.*

Or, *What if it's possible for me to accept all of this, and to be open to new insights
and to experiencing something else.*

Get Curious

I feel curious about _____

_____

_____

_____

In my body, I notice _____

_____

_____

Get Creative

Refuturing Statements:

♥ *What if it's possible* _____

♥ *What if it's possible* _____

♥ *What if it's possible* _____

♥ *What if it's possible* _____

♥ *What if it's possible* _____

Do the Heart Center Pose and say your Refuturing Statements aloud.

I choose _____

Say your Choose Statement several times aloud,
ideally while doing the Power Pose and looking into a mirror.

When I open to the Universe _____

_____

_____

_____

Get Courageous

What's next? _____

*My **one** next step is to* _____

_____

_____

I'll do it by _____

Do the Heart Center Pose and imagine yourself taking the action you just wrote about.

I feel _____

_____

In my body, I notice _____

_____

Write the action on your calendar. Do the Power Pose and *feel* yourself completing it.

Tranquil

Acknowledge Your Feelings

I feel tranquil about _____
_____
_____
_____
_____
_____
_____
_____
_____
_____

Do the Heart Center Pose and say: *I accept all of these feelings.*
Or, *What if it's possible for me to accept all of these feelings?*

In my body, I notice _____
_____
_____

Move your body

Do the Energy Hookup.

Do the Heart Center Pose and say: *I accept all of this, and I'm open to new insights*
    and to experiencing something else.

Or, *What if it's possible for me to accept all of this, and to be open to new insights*
    and to experiencing something else.

Get Curious

I feel curious about _____
_____
_____
_____

In my body, I notice _____
_____
_____

Get Creative

Refuturing Statements:

♥ *What if it's possible* _____

♥ *What if it's possible* _____

♥ *What if it's possible* _____

♥ *What if it's possible* _____

♥ *What if it's possible* _____

Do the Heart Center Pose and say your Refuturing Statements aloud.

I choose _____

Say your Choose Statement several times aloud,
ideally while doing the Power Pose and looking into a mirror.

When I open to the Universe _____

_____

_____

_____

Get Courageous

What's next? _____

*My **one** next step is to* _____

_____

I'll do it by _____

Do the Heart Center Pose and imagine yourself taking the action you just wrote about.

I feel _____

_____

In my body, I notice _____

_____

Write the action on your calendar. Do the Power Pose and *feel* yourself completing it.

Grateful

Acknowledge Your Feelings

I feel grateful about _____

_____

_____

_____

_____

_____

_____

_____

_____

Do the Heart Center Pose and say: *I accept all of these feelings.*
Or, *What if it's possible for me to accept all of these feelings?*

In my body, I notice _____

_____

_____

Move your body

Do the Energy Hookup.

Do the Heart Center Pose and say: *I accept all of this, and I'm open to new insights and to experiencing something else.*

Or, *What if it's possible for me to accept all of this, and to be open to new insights and to experiencing something else.*

Get Curious

I feel curious about _____

_____

_____

In my body, I notice _____

_____

_____

Get Creative

Refuturing Statements:

♥ *What if it's possible* _____

♥ *What if it's possible* _____

♥ *What if it's possible* _____

♥ *What if it's possible* _____

♥ *What if it's possible* _____

Do the Heart Center Pose and say your Refuturing Statements aloud.

I choose _____

**Say your Choose Statement several times aloud,
ideally while doing the Power Pose and looking into a mirror.**

When I open to the Universe _____

_____

_____

_____

Get Courageous

What's next? _____

My **one** *next step is to* _____

_____

I'll do it by _____

Do the Heart Center Pose and imagine yourself taking the action you just wrote about.

I feel _____

_____

In my body, I notice _____

_____

Write the action on your calendar. Do the Power Pose and *feel* yourself completing it.

Grateful

Acknowledge Your Feelings

I feel grateful about _____

_____

_____

_____

_____

_____

_____

_____

_____

_____

Do the Heart Center Pose and say: *I accept all of these feelings.*
Or, *What if it's possible for me to accept all of these feelings?*

In my body, I notice _____

_____

_____

Move your body

Do the Energy Hookup.

Do the Heart Center Pose and say: *I accept all of this, and I'm open to new insights
    and to experiencing something else.*
Or, *What if it's possible for me to accept all of this, and to be open to new insights
    and to experiencing something else.*

Get Curious

I feel curious about _____

_____

_____

_____

In my body, I notice _____

_____

_____

Get Creative

Refuturing Statements:

♥ *What if it's possible* _____

♥ *What if it's possible* _____

♥ *What if it's possible* _____

♥ *What if it's possible* _____

♥ *What if it's possible* _____

Do the Heart Center Pose and say your Refuturing Statements aloud.

I choose _____

**Say your Choose Statement several times aloud,
ideally while doing the Power Pose and looking into a mirror.**

When I open to the Universe _____

_____

_____

_____

Get Courageous

What's next? _____

*My **one** next step is to* _____

_____

_____

I'll do it by _____

Do the Heart Center Pose and imagine yourself taking the action you just wrote about.

I feel _____

_____

In my body, I notice _____

_____

Write the action on your calendar. Do the Power Pose and *feel* yourself completing it.

Relaxed

Acknowledge Your Feelings

I feel relaxed about _____

_____

_____

_____

_____

_____

_____

_____

_____

Do the Heart Center Pose and say: *I accept all of these feelings.*
Or, *What if it's possible for me to accept all of these feelings?*

In my body, I notice _____

_____

_____

Move your body

Do the Energy Hookup.

Do the Heart Center Pose and say: *I accept all of this, and I'm open to new insights
and to experiencing something else.*

Or, *What if it's possible for me to accept all of this, and to be open to new insights
and to experiencing something else.*

Get Curious

I feel curious about _____

_____

_____

_____

In my body, I notice _____

_____

_____

Get Creative

Refuturing Statements:

♥ *What if it's possible* _____

♥ *What if it's possible* _____

♥ *What if it's possible* _____

♥ *What if it's possible* _____

♥ *What if it's possible* _____

Do the Heart Center Pose and say your Refuturing Statements aloud.

I choose _____

**Say your Choose Statement several times aloud,
ideally while doing the Power Pose and looking into a mirror.**

When I open to the Universe _____

_____

_____

_____

Get Courageous

What's next? _____

*My **one** next step is to* _____

_____

_____

I'll do it by _____

Do the Heart Center Pose and imagine yourself taking the action you just wrote about.

I feel _____

_____

In my body, I notice _____

_____

Write the action on your calendar. Do the Power Pose and *feel* yourself completing it.

Relaxed

Acknowledge Your Feelings

I feel relaxed about _____
_____
_____
_____
_____
_____
_____
_____
_____
_____

Do the Heart Center Pose and say: *I accept all of these feelings.*
Or, *What if it's possible for me to accept all of these feelings?*

In my body, I notice _____
_____

Move your body

Do the Energy Hookup.

Do the Heart Center Pose and say: *I accept all of this, and I'm open to new insights and to experiencing something else.*

Or, *What if it's possible for me to accept all of this, and to be open to new insights and to experiencing something else.*

Get Curious

I feel curious about _____
_____
_____
_____

In my body, I notice _____
_____
_____

Get Creative

Refuturing Statements:

♥ *What if it's possible* _____

♥ *What if it's possible* _____

♥ *What if it's possible* _____

♥ *What if it's possible* _____

♥ *What if it's possible* _____

Do the Heart Center Pose and say your Refuturing Statements aloud.

I choose _____

**Say your Choose Statement several times aloud,
ideally while doing the Power Pose and looking into a mirror.**

When I open to the Universe _____

_____

_____

_____

Get Courageous

What's next? _____

*My **one** next step is to* _____

_____

I'll do it by _____

Do the Heart Center Pose and imagine yourself taking the action you just wrote about.

I feel _____

_____

In my body, I notice _____

_____

Write the action on your calendar. Do the Power Pose and *feel* yourself completing it.

In Harmony With

Acknowledge Your Feelings

I feel in harmony with _____

_____

_____

_____

_____

_____

_____

_____

_____

Do the Heart Center Pose and say: *I accept all of these feelings.*
Or, *What if it's possible for me to accept all of these feelings?*

In my body, I notice _____

_____

_____

Move your body

Do the Energy Hookup.

Do the Heart Center Pose and say: *I accept all of this, and I'm open to new insights
and to experiencing something else.*

Or, *What if it's possible for me to accept all of this, and to be open to new insights
and to experiencing something else.*

Get Curious

I feel curious about _____

_____

_____

_____

In my body, I notice _____

_____

_____

Get Creative

Refuturing Statements:

♥ *What if it's possible* _____

♥ *What if it's possible* _____

♥ *What if it's possible* _____

♥ *What if it's possible* _____

♥ *What if it's possible* _____

Do the Heart Center Pose and say your Refuturing Statements aloud.

I choose _____

**Say your Choose Statement several times aloud,
ideally while doing the Power Pose and looking into a mirror.**

When I open to the Universe _____

_____

_____

_____

Get Courageous

What's next? _____

*My **one** next step is to* _____

_____

_____

I'll do it by _____

Do the Heart Center Pose and imagine yourself taking the action you just wrote about.

I feel _____

_____

In my body, I notice _____

_____

Write the action on your calendar. Do the Power Pose and *feel* yourself completing it.

In Harmony With

Acknowledge Your Feelings

I feel in harmony with _____

_____

_____

_____

_____

_____

_____

_____

_____

Do the Heart Center Pose and say: *I accept all of these feelings.*
Or, *What if it's possible for me to accept all of these feelings?*

In my body, I notice _____

_____

_____

Move your body

Do the Energy Hookup.

Do the Heart Center Pose and say: *I accept all of this, and I'm open to new insights
and to experiencing something else.*

Or, *What if it's possible for me to accept all of this, and to be open to new insights
and to experiencing something else.*

Get Curious

I feel curious about _____

_____

_____

In my body, I notice _____

_____

_____

Get Creative

Refuturing Statements:

♥ *What if it's possible* _____

♥ *What if it's possible* _____

♥ *What if it's possible* _____

♥ *What if it's possible* _____

♥ *What if it's possible* _____

Do the Heart Center Pose and say your Refuturing Statements aloud.

I choose _____

Say your Choose Statement several times aloud,
ideally while doing the Power Pose and looking into a mirror.

When I open to the Universe _____

_____

_____

_____

Get Courageous

What's next? _____

*My **one** next step is to* _____

_____

_____

I'll do it by _____

Do the Heart Center Pose and imagine yourself taking the action you just wrote about.

I feel _____

_____

In my body, I notice _____

_____

Write the action on your calendar. Do the Power Pose and *feel* yourself completing it.

Appendix

Refuturing Statements

What if it's possible that I am okay.

What if it's possible that I am safe.

What if it's possible I'm just where I need to be.

What if it's possible that my feelings are temporary.

What if it's possible I'm more powerful than I realize.

What if it's possible for me to feel scared and excited.

What if it's possible for me to feel angry and hopeful.

What if it's possible for me to feel discouraged and confident.

What if it's possible that I am more than my feelings.

What if it's possible that I am more than my thoughts.

What if it's possible there is an eternal part of me that is bigger than I dreamed possible.

What if it's possible I'm always connected with the eternal part of me.

What if it's possible that I'm always connected to others.

What if it's possible that no matter how alone I feel at times,
    I'm always, always connected to others.

What if it's possible that I'm always connected to my power.

What if it's possible that I'm always connected to the Divine.

What if it's possible that things can be different.

What if it's possible that I have more power in this situation than I realize.

What if it's possible that I have more options right now than I realize.

What if it's possible I can do things differently.

What if it's possible I can make different choices.

What if it's possible for me to claim and exercise more power in this situation.

What if it's possible for me to be loving and compassionate with myself.

What if it's possible that being loving and gentle with myself opens new possibilities for me.

What if it's possible that there are parts of this situation that I don't understand yet.

What if it's possible that I don't know everything.

What if it's possible that this situation is here for me and my highest good.

What if it's possible that this situation is helping me to expand.

What if it's possible for me to feel grateful, even in the midst of this.

What if it's possible for me to accept all the love, wonder, and joy available to me right now.

What if it's possible for me to open my heart.

What if it's possible that there is great strength in gentleness and kindness.

What if it's possible that there is great strength in love.

What if it's possible that there is enough for me.

What if it's possible that I am enough.

What if it's possible that I have gifts and talents I haven't discovered yet.

What if it's possible I have infinite creativity.

What if it's possible that it's safe for me to shine.

What if it's possible that my whole energy system is shifting, and getting stronger and brighter.

What if it's possible it's safe for me to be in my heart.

What if it's possible that I am more supported, loved, and held than I realize.

What if it's possible I can do this, and that I am ready to do this.

Choose Statements

I choose to be in my body and embrace new security and new possibility.

I choose to trust money, the Universe, and myself.

I choose to use my voice to express ME.

I choose to remember that I am safe and supported.

I choose to play possibilities.

I choose to trust, surrender, and ride the waves.

I choose to embrace and enjoy the possibilities as they continue to unfold.

I choose to be a _____ (mom, employee, CEO) without losing myself.

I choose to breathe, relax, and trust, allowing myself to shine as all that I am.

I choose to play with new possibilities, with joy, ease, and gentleness, knowing
    that I am not my past and not bound by the patterns of my ancestors.

I choose to release what doesn't serve me and to trust my own path.

I choose to play with possibilities with curiosity, compassion, and joy.

I choose to be open to and welcoming of possibilities, my intuition, my feelings, and myself.

I choose to play, trust, breathe deeply, and love myself right where I am today.

I choose to dance, love, and laugh with all of me.

I choose life, love, and me.

I choose to embrace the process of reclaiming my power, and to do it
    with gentleness, compassion, love, acceptance, and support.

I choose to love and value the imperfect me, allowing the
    abundance of my love to flow out to others.

I choose to follow my process and exploration with lightness, joy, and ease.

I choose to be curious, clear, compassionate, loving, and steady.

I choose to play with the possibilities of love, forgiveness, action, and abundance.

I choose to relax into the flow and allow it to be safe and easy for me to shine.

I choose to relax, feel my feelings, and be gentle with myself.

I choose to embrace and be present with all the parts of me,
    as I take steps each day to follow my bliss.

I choose to accept and embrace all of me, blessing and
    releasing those who aren't a fit with me.

I choose to allow and embrace all of me with openness, spaciousness, and possibility.

I choose to own my full power and my value in my business and my life.

I choose to be open to the possibility that I am valuable, seen, and significant just as I am.

I choose to be playful.

I choose to work my way.

I choose to serve others with joy and not suffering

I choose joy, play, and productivity every day.

I choose the possibility of forgiving and trusting myself, my body, and my abundance.

I choose to embrace and dance with my possibilities of connection, joy, and ease.

I choose to stand in my higher self and create from there.

I choose to relax, allow, receive, create, and enjoy.

I choose to relax, be in my body, and accept my own strength.

I choose to share and receive with passion, strength, fun, flow, & ease.

I choose to take up my rightful space and shine.

I choose to be in my body, feel my emotions, and embrace my power.

I Am Courageous Enough Statements

I am courageous enough to be my full self.

I am courageous enough to be uncomfortable.

I am courageous enough to be uncertain.

I am courageous enough to live my truth.

I am courageous enough to step into the unknown.

I am courageous enough to express my heart.

I am courageous enough to truly listen to others

I am courageous enough to listen to myself.

I am courageous enough to be me.

I am courageous enough to be with my pain.

I am courageous enough to accept my heart.

I am courageous enough to love myself.

I am courageous enough to accept all of myself.

I am courageous enough to communicate clearly.

I am courageous enough to ask for what I want.

I am courageous enough to be authentic.

I am courageous enough to hold my boundaries.

I am courageous enough to respect my needs.

I am courageous enough to be generous.

I am courageous enough to be compassionate.

I am courageous enough to listen to feedback.

I am courageous enough to accept help.

I am courageous enough to celebrate my accomplishments.

I am courageous enough to own my strengths, gifts, and talents.

I am courageous enough to have hope.

I am courageous enough to dream big.

I am courageous enough to say "no".

I am courageous enough to say "yes".

I am courageous enough to say "I don't know."

I am courageous enough to say "I know."

I am courageous enough to be honest.

I am courageous enough to do things differently.

I am courageous enough to experience something different.

I am courageous enough to release what doesn't serve me.

I am courageous enough to embrace what I love.

I am courageous enough to be joyful.

I am courageous enough to make changes in my life.

I am courageous enough to be patient.

I am courageous enough to speak up.

I am courageous enough to see another's point of view.

I am courageous enough to share my ideas.

I am courageous enough to listen to others' ideas.

I am courageous enough to be successful.

I am courageous enough to be present in each moment.

I am courageous enough to be honest.

I am courageous enough to be caring.

I am courageous enough to be kind.

I am courageous enough to be compassionate.

I am courageous enough to stand up for my beliefs.

I am courageous enough to allow others their beliefs.

I am courageous enough to respect the humanity of all.

I am courageous enough to be prosperous.

I am courageous enough to be wealthy.

I am courageous enough to feel.

I am courageous enough to acknowledge and accept my fears.

I am courageous enough not to be stopped by my fears.

I am courageous enough to accept my reality.

I am courageous enough to accept that my reality can change quickly.

I am courageous enough to accept and build on what's happening in my life right now.

I am courageous enough to be generous in thought, word, and deed.

I am courageous enough to be vulnerable.

I am courageous enough to love.

I am courageous enough to be loved.

I am courageous enough to dance.

I am courageous enough to stand up straight.

I am courageous enough to take action.

I am courageous enough to love the person I am.

I am courageous enough to stand on my own.

I am courageous enough to trust myself.

I am courageous enough to believe in myself.

I am courageous enough to decide.

I am courageous enough to choose.

I am courageous enough to be intuitive.

I am courageous enough to be inspired.

I am courageous enough to follow my inner guidance.

I am courageous enough to be authentic.

I am courageous enough to be real.

I am courageous enough to change my mind.

I am courageous enough to stick with my decision and what I know.

I am courageous enough to walk my path.

I am courageous enough to do hard things.

I am courageous enough to do new things.

I am courageous enough to do bold things.

I am courageous enough to do uncomfortable things.

I am courageous enough to create.

I am courageous enough to relax.

I am courageous enough to not be perfect.

I am courageous enough to be awesome.

I am courageous enough to not be liked.

I am courageous enough to be liked.

I am courageous enough to take risks.

I am courageous enough to be humble.

I am courageous enough to apologize.

I am courageous enough to forgive.

I am courageous enough to be strong.

I am courageous enough to confident.

I am courageous enough to gentle.

I am courageous enough to be beautiful.

I am courageous enough to be eccentric.

I am courageous enough to be intelligent.

I am courageous enough to be friendly.

I am courageous enough to be quiet.

I am courageous enough to be awkward.

I am courageous enough to be graceful.

I am courageous enough to be bold.

I am courageous enough to be sexy.

I am courageous enough to lead.

I am courageous enough to lead myself.

I am courageous enough to rest.

I am courageous enough to be peaceful.

I am courageous enough to be silent.

I am courageous enough to live abundantly.

I am courageous enough to speak my truth.

I Am Statements

I am wise.

I am curious.

I am creative.

I am courageous.

I am hopeful.

I am delightful.

I am energetic.

I am radiant.

I am vibrant.

I am beautiful.

I am handsome.

I am powerful.

I am clear.

I am generous.

I am generous in thought, word, and action.

I am supportive of others.

I am trusting.

I am quiet.

I am at peace.

I am magical.

I am mystical.

I am magnificent.

I am happy.

I am abundant.

I am worthy.

I am good enough.

I am enough.

I am more than enough.

I am present.

I am compassionate.

I am loving.

I am loved.

I am bold.

I am soft.

I am powerful.

I am joyful.

I am at ease.

I am playful.

I am fun.

I am capable of great things.

I am a champion of those around me.

I am gracious.

I am supported.

I am guided.

I am grounded.

I am radiantly healthy.

I am warm.

I am welcoming.

I am myself.

I am magnetic.

I am mindful.

I am attractive.

I am effective.

I am approachable.

I am in tune with my heart.

I am living from my wisest self.

I am affectionate.

I am in my power.

I am expansive.

I am confident.

I am spacious.

I am connected with my feelings.

I am connected with my body.

I am connected with all of me.

I am connected with all of life.

I am surrounded by beauty.

I am surrounded by love.

I am surrounded by people who love me.

I am surrounded by people who support me.

I am surrounded by opportunities.

I am strong in my yes.

I am strong in my no.

I am living my purpose.

I am living my dreams.

I am open to new possibilities.

I am open to new experiences.

I am open to new friendships.

I am open to new stories.

I am open to new insights.

I am open to new ideas.

I am open to new ways of being.

I am receptive.

I am someone who listens deeply and attentively.

I am someone who speaks with clarity and confidence.

I am good enough for all of my dreams.

I am worthy of all my dreams and goals.

I am worthy of being seen.

I am worthy of being heard.

I am worthy of taking up the space that's mine to fill.

I am worthy of being loved.

I am worthy of money and abundance.

I am worthy of help, support, and opportunities.

I am worthy of shining and sharing.

I am grounded in the present moment.

I am attentive and observant.

I am strong.

I am flexible.

I am wholehearted.

I am love.

I am willing to see things differently.

I am willing to accept my life as it currently is.

I am willing to do things differently.

I am willing to be all of who I am.

I am all of this and much, much more.